Celebrating with the European Cup.

Four First Division Championship trophies have been won, too of course, but perhaps the honours which have given Terry most pleasure are The Football Writers' Player of the Year and the Players' Player of the Year awards, both of which were won in 1980.

Printed and published in Great Britain
by D. C. THOMSON & CO. LTD.
185, Fleet St. London, EC4A 2HS
© D. C. THOMSON & CO. LTD. 1981
ISBN 0 85116 209 6

£1·65

It's action all the way

There are thrills and excitement in our sports picture stories. Like STARK, for instance!

An in-depth focus on Grand Prix ace, ALAN JONES.

Tremendous CRICKETING action with the brilliant West Indians.

Our own special tribute to the "King of Tennis"— BJORN BORG.

...and there's much, much

Speed ace KENNY ROBERTS as you've never seen him before.

BALLESTEROS and NICKLAUS, giants of the golfing world.

We've got guest-writers galore, too. Big-name players like GRAHAM RIX, STAN CUMMINS & KENNY DALGLISH, to name but three of our all-star, all-sport line-up!

And don't forget the pin-ups which feature many top stars like KEVIN KEEGAN.

more besides! Get reading!

STARK

MATCHWINNER FOR HIRE — JON STARK

£1500 PER MATCH
PLUS £250 PER GOAL

NO PAYMENT FOR LOST GAME

Stark's scored again! Why weren't you covering him?

You're joking. It's like marking a ghost!

Full time . . .

Now to begin my training programme for my Cup Final game with City next Saturday. I'm really looking forward to playing for Mike Carswell and his boys.

But when Stark returns to his flat . . .

A letter from City's opponents, Rovers. Paterson, their manager, says I'm contracted to play five games for them. And he wants them all played next week! What's he up to?

Paterson was a shady character who'd been suspended from football for a two-year period . . .

What are you on about, Paterson? I never signed any contract with the Rovers.

True, Stark, but take a look at the contract you signed with me when I was boss of Albion. It's rock solid.

WHAT A HAT-TRICK!

Stark visits his lawyer . . .

'Fraid it's binding, Jon. When Albion folded, the contract with Paterson came into effect.

Which means I'll have to report to Rovers or be sued.

That allthough contracted primarily to play for Albion, should the aforesaid five games not be played, Jon Stark will be legally bound to play in five matches for Noel Paterson.

Monday . . .

Get aboard, Stark . . . the reserves have a friendly today. Your contract is no fee for a lost game or a nil-nil draw.

Or £1500 for a win and £250 per goal. I'll make you pay, Paterson.

Bighead! It'll be worth what little I do pay. I can't play you myself on Saturday but I'll make darn sure you're so tired you won't be fit to play for City against us in the Cup Final.

8

Stark scores four! On the bus after the match . . .

Sorry I wasn't able to give you more support, Jon. I'm working my way back into the game after an injury.

That's okay, Georgie. You've got talent. How'd you like a private session with me to iron out a few wrinkles?

That evening . . .

A belter, Georgie. Nice ball.

He's good. And he learns fast.

The following evening Stark plays for Rovers' first team in a league match . . .

Stark's the only man up front. He could run himself to a standstill in that muddy pitch and never score.

Blast!

Don't you want the ball, Stark?

Patience is the thing, friend.

And five minutes from time . . .

The waiting game's paid off. This pass-back's short.

That's £1750 I've cost Paterson – without using too much energy!

Wednesday. Stark plays for the reserves . . .

A lovely pass. Coaching young Georgie Milburn has paid off!

ON TOP OF THE WORLD

GREAT MOMENTS IN SPORT 1966

It was the day that England, the founders of football, again became its masters. Hosts of the 1966 World Cup Finals, England met West Germany, who had previously won the trophy in 1954, in what turned out to be one of the most dramatic matches ever played at Wembley.

As the game moved into the last minute, England were leading 2-1 and preparing to be acclaimed World Champions — when disaster struck. In a packed England penalty area, the Germans scrambled an equaliser and sent the final into extra-time for the first time since 1934.

Could manager Alf Ramsay lift his players for the extra thirty minutes? The answer was yes — thanks to the determination of skipper Bobby Moore, the running of Martin Peters and Bobby Charlton, the sharpshooting of Geoff Hurst . . . and the decision of a Russian linesman!

As play swung from one end to the other, Hurst broke through the German defence, launched a shot which beat the keeper but which crashed against the underside of the bar and was cleared by a German defender as it bounced back into play. "Goal!" claimed England. The Germans protested and a silence fell over the stadium as the referee, unsighted, consulted his linesman.

Seconds later, Wembley erupted. England were indeed a goal ahead, and with almost the last kick of the game Geoff Hurst repeated the dose to become the scorer of the first-ever World Cup Final hat trick and secure a 4-2 victory.

England were on top of the world!

Last-minute disaster as Weber turns the ball into the England net to force the final into extra-time.

Did the ball cross the line? Roger Hunt looks on anxiously as Geoff Hurst's shot smacks the underside of the bar — and England are awarded their third goal.

Hat-trick hero Hurst puts the game beyond doubt — with a fourth goal in the dying seconds of the match.

World Champions England! Captain Bobby Moore celebrates with keeper Gordon Banks.

TALL, DARK...

Jamaica, Barbados, Guyana, Trinidad, Antigua... far-off Caribbean islands which conjure up dreams of sunshine, beaches and limbo dancing. But they also breed a unique type of sportsman capable of skills rarely matched anywhere else in the world—the West Indian Cricketer!

Cricket history is filled with such men, but never in years gone by have the West Indies had such a brilliant attacking side as they do now.

Power and pace are their trademarks, and hard-bitten Aussies, technically correct Englishmen, and the subtle skills of the Asians have all been blasted out of their cricket pads by a set of bowlers who make faster deliveries than Concorde, and a batting line-up who wouldn't take long to wrap up America's National Baseball League should they ever decide to change sports!

Their six feet plus brigade of "quickies", Croft, Marshall, Garner, Roberts and Holding, treat batsmen with the contempt they don't deserve, and a ball bowled at anything less than eighty miles per hour is considered a "bad 'un" in their book!

In a word, their batsmen are superb, and we've long since run out of superlatives to describe the perfection of Viv Richards and his flamboyant, bat-swinging mates.

But while bowling and batting come naturally to the men from these sun-drenched islands, their apparant "laziness" in the field is perhaps their one weakness. Catches get dropped, batsmen steal extra runs as gangling W. Indies players just amble over the outfield, and poor throw-ins send wicket keeper Deryck Murray scurrying further than he should.

Mind you, with devastating bowlers and matchwinning batsmen, who needs good fielders anyway!?

FAOUD BACCHUS—introduced to this country on the West Indies 1980 tour and quickly established himself as one of the finest fielders in the game.

Occasionally a slow starter, but DESMOND HAYNES is dynamite once he gets his eye in!

and DEADLY!

MALCOLM MARSHALL—
One of the new breed of
West Indian "quickies",
and a player who's sure to
be around for many years to
come.

At 6 ft. 8 in. tall, JOEL GARNER
is the giant of the West Indies squad.
He's also a giant when it comes to
taking Test wickets—as many of the
England team will testify!

Perhaps the fastest bowler of
them all, that's MICHAEL
HOLDING, but his greatest
assets are his accuracy and
length.

No introduction needed for this all-
time great. It's just VIV RICHARDS
cracking away another four!

KLOG

NORMAN!

YES, BOSS?

YOU'RE LETTING THEIR STAR, GLENN RUBBLE, DOMINATE THE MIDFIELD.

SORRY, BOSS. D'YOU WANT ME TO KICK HIS KNEES?

NORMAN, NORMAN. IS THIS WHAT OUR ONCE-GREAT GAME HAS COME TO? MINDLESS VIOLENCE?

NO, I WANT YOU TO SLIP THESE KNOCKOUT DROPS IN HIS HALF-TIME CUPPA!

KEVIN KEEGAN

"Technically, I'm the worst player to win the European Player of the Year award. I've had to learn to live with my limitations. What has got me through is my work rate."

B

ANY form of motor sport is tough, not only for the men involved but also for the machines they drive. Damage of all kinds – from a slight dent to a whole new body – is common, but rarely has anyone seen a car more spectacularly wrecked than in this crash which took place during a race between Ford Fiestas at Brands Hatch!

SPEED SCENE

WRITE-OFF!

The beginning — Stevie Taylor loses control . . .

. . . slews round on its side . . .

. . . crashes down . . .

. . . crunches down on its roof . . .

. . . and turns upright again!

. . . and turns over!

The tail-gate flies open as the car . . .

. . . and "bounces" — with wheels flying off and windows shattering!

It's not finished yet as the car goes over . . .

It's all over! The total destruction of the Fiesta is complete and the car comes to rest at the side of the track.

The marshalls and rescue team rush in to release the driver. Incredibly, Stevie Taylor is unharmed! Surely one of the luckiest men on the motor sport scene!

These pictures were shot by a sixteen-year-old called ANDREW EDMUNDS. Amazingly enough, it was one of his first-ever attempts at action photography!

I LOVE PLAYING FOOTBALL

One of the easiest things in football is to take it easy once you've made it to the top. But that's a danger Arsenal's star midfielder Graham Rix always guards against.

" Just like everybody else I love success," Graham told Scoop, " but I never forget how lucky I am to be playing in top-class football with a club like Arsenal. I've had opportunities to see the world and enjoy life that most people only dream about.

" But I've had bad times as well and I think I've learned from them. For instance, everybody asks me how it felt to play in the Cup Final in 1979 when Arsenal won that great match against Manchester United by a narrow 3-2 margin. And the answer is of course, just fantastic. But the previous year was a different story altogether.

" Arsenal were in the F.A. Cup Final that year as well. I'd played in 39 out of the sides 42 league games that season but when it came to the big one the boss named me as substitute.

" Of course, the manager has every right to choose the team he thinks is right for the occasion, but I won't pretend it wasn't a big blow to me. The thing is though, was that it made me all the more determined to get in on the action in the future. So the Cup Final the following year was a great day for me."

But the Cup Finals apart there's another big reason why Graham thanks his lucky stars every time he steps on to a pitch . . .

" Yes, I know that I'm very lucky to be fit enough to play the game at all. I remember when I was about eighteen, I picked up a bad back injury. When you've cracked two vertebrae in your spine you naturally begin to wonder if you'll ever play again. And when you're in a plaster cast for three months you've plenty of time to build up thoughts of doom and disaster in your mind! All in all, that was a bad time.

" But I was lucky, I made a good recovery. My comeback match with the reserves was a bit scary of course, but I came through that first test all right and the whole thing's just made me determined to show everybody what I can do."

You've only got to go along to Highbury now to see that Graham can do plenty to set the crowd roaring. Skilful on the ball and with the ability to lay off the ball to a team-mate with superb precision.

" Of course, it's difficult for me to judge my own strengths and weaknesses as a player. I think I should score more goals and sometimes I lack a bit of concentration.

" But on the positive side I work hard in keeping my attitude right. For instance, some people think I'm a bit frail-looking but I think my positive attitude makes up for lack of brawn. I hope so anyway, and I'm always working hard at my game, trying to improve.

" Any success I have had though owes a lot to the people who worked hard to bring the best out of me when I first came to London as a youngster. There were lots of course. But if I had to pick out two, there's Don Howe. He's a tremendous coach, knows the game inside out. Then there's Sammy Nelson. He had a big effect on my game, playing behind me.

" Another big help was that when I broke into first team football, so did Frank Stapleton and David O'Leary. We'd all played in the same youth team, so the togetherness we'd built up there helped a lot.

" All in all I've never regretted signing for Arsenal, though I was born in Doncaster and as a kid I wanted to play for Leeds. I even went to Elland Road for a trial.

" But it was the standard of coaching at Highbury that attracted me. The facilities too, are so good. I remember when I first came down to the club and sat in the famous marble hall. Everybody was rushing around, the place looked like an hotel!

" It was all a bit overawing. But when I settled in I found all the other apprentices and the first team players really friendly. And still today Arsenal's a happy club to play with."

Apart from his club commitments though, Graham has made good progress at international level. After only fourteen first team games he won his first Under-21 Cap by coming on as substitute against Finland!

Since then he's moved up the ladder and been capped at full international level . . . " I remember my international debut," Graham recalled. " It was against Norway at Wembley and we won 4-0. It was a good match to earn my spurs in. Everybody expected England to win and there wasn't a lot of pressure. I enjoyed every minute of the game.

" As for my aims for the future, well, someday I might be interested in coaching but first I want to win as much as I can at club level, and with England—well, I always look on that as a bonus on top of my club commitments—but there are the World Cup Finals in Spain coming up. If England are there then of course I'd like to be part of the plans.

" But whatever happens at club or international level, I know how lucky I am to be doing what I love doing most—playing football!

SCOTCH CORNER

SCOTLAND'S

ASK almost any schoolboy mad keen on football what he'd like to be and his reply is almost certainly to be "a professional footballer." It's a dream shared by many. But what's it really like when the opportunity comes your way? Two of Scotland's greatest young players, JOHN MACDONALD of RANGERS and CHARLIE NICHOLAS of CELTIC, tell Scoop readers what it's like to fulfil that boyhood dream.

JOHN...

"I WAS an 'S' signing for Rangers when I was fourteen and to be connected with the club I'd always supported was great. Saturday was the best day of the week, I'd play for my school team in the morning and Clydebank Strollers, a juvenile team, in the afternoon. But the best time of the year was school holidays, not because I was off, but it meant I would be training at Ibrox. There were about seven or eight 'S' signings who came in for these full-time stints. It was fantastic to train with the real professionals, and the manager (Jock Wallace at that time) didn't keep us out of things, we mixed in with the real professionals."

DECISION TIME

"That was more or less how my football career continued for the next two or three years until I was in my fifth year at school. It was early 1978 and I knew I'd be leaving school in the summer. Decision time was approaching regarding my future as a footballer as I was seventeen on the 15th of April. Football was all I thought about and it was this very thing that put me out of action for the first time in my short career. I was having trouble with my stomach and the doctor at Ibrox told me I was thinking and playing too much football. I suppose I was worried whether or not I was going to be asked to sign for Rangers but Jock Wallace soon put my mind at rest.

One Saturday I was in watching the first team play when the boss said he was going to put me on a "form." However, assistant manager Willie Thornton pointed out that that would prevent me playing for the juveniles for the rest of the season, and we'd be better to wait.

"It wasn't long after this that Jock Wallace left Ibrox and John Greig became manager. However, the club still wanted me and when I left school in July I signed full professional forms for Glasgow Rangers. It was absolutely marvellous to sign for them. A dream come true — and a great relief!"

A FIRST-TEAM PLACE

"I was fortunate to be included in the squad that went on a Highland tour at the beginning of the next season and I was listed as substitute for the games. For most of the following season I spent much of my time in the reserves, but I managed to score twelve goals. The boss put me on the substitute bench a couple of times though for the first team against Motherwell in a Scottish Cup tie and a league game versus Hearts.

"Playing professional football is entirely different from what you're used to as a juvenile. The standard is obviously higher, your opponents don't make the same basic errors, and they're strong too. But the full-time training has also made me physically tougher. I've not developed huge muscles or anything like that but the weight circuits at Ibrox give you strength.

"It was after a tough pre-season training period in 1979 that I got a chance in the first team. I was substitute in the first two games of the Drybrough Cup against

JOHN MACDONALD

Berwick and Kilmarnock. In the match with Killie I came on and managed to score both goals in our 2-0 win. To my delight the boss listed me in the Final team against Celtic. We won 3-1 and I got one of the goals! It was a wonderful feeling."

BIG HEADED? NO WAY!

"Over the next few months, I was used mainly as a substitute for the first team but it was a great boost to be part of the squad.

"I'm often asked if playing for Rangers and being a youngster makes you big headed? Well, in my case I can honestly say no — John Greig or Joe Mason would soon knock it out of me! Speaking about Joe, he and the manager have been a great influence on me. I've learnt a lot from them. Of course, you also learn a lot from the older, experienced players. Sandy Jardine is one such player and he's given me a lot of help.

"It's when you first come

SUPER STARLETS

into the team the older players play a big part. They encourage you, let you know when you've made a mistake and in general help you through the game.

"At the moment, I'm playing as a striker. I used to play mostly on the wing when I was younger (the left, because my right foot was only good for standing on), but just to be in the team is enough for me and I would play anywhere!"

Honest words from a young, highly-talented player, and now we switch to the other half of Glasgow to listen to . . .

CHARLIE...

"**M**Y first association with Celtic was not unlike John's with Rangers. I was on a schoolboy form but I played for the club's nursery side as well, Celtic Boys Club. I suppose this helped them to keep a closer watch on my progress. After I left school in 1978 I started an apprenticeship as a motor mechanic. I still wanted to be a professional footballer more than anything else but I knew I needed some sort of career in case my dream didn't come true. I enjoyed working as a mechanic, doing my training at Parkhead at night and playing on a Saturday for the Boys Club.

"I was scoring goals regularly for the Under-18s and in the March of 1979 Mr McNeill asked me to have a week's trial, training full time with the rest of the players. I jumped at the chance. That week was superb and I managed to score a couple of goals in practice matches. It was after this I was offered the chance to become a professional footballer. As you can probably guess, I couldn't wait to put pen to paper. I'd supported Celtic all my life and it had always been my ambition to play for them — and now the day had arrived. I felt 'magic,' that's the only way I can describe it!"

LEARNING MY "TRADE"

"Over the next year I played regularly for the reserves as a striker. During

CHARLIE NICHOLAS

season '79-'80 I played thirty matches and scored, with the help of my team-mates, twenty-seven goals.

"During this time I was learning a lot about the game. It was so different from playing against boys your own age. The first thing I noticed was your opponents kicked you a lot harder. You learn not to dwell too long on the ball when someone's coming charging in. The full-time training was having its effect, though. I was so much fitter, I felt as if I could run all day. I'm not particularly

well-built but I was physically stronger. Frank Connor, who's now manager at Berwick, looked after the reserves at Parkhead and he possibly, with the exception of my dad, helped me more than anyone else in my career. His coaching, encouragement and words of warning all contributed to my step-up to the first team. Billy McNeill, my manager, obviously has helped me a lot and I have the greatest respect for him.

"He used me as substitute a few times for the first team

at the tail-end of '79-'80 and I actually played from the start in the Glasgow Cup against Queen's Park and Clyde. We won both games and I was fortunate enough to score in the two matches. It was a great thrill to be a part of the big team.

"The close season came around and I could hardly wait to get started again in July. I trained hard and the boss couldn't have given me a better reward — I was in the squad to go on a tour to Germany and Holland. I had a couple of appearances as substitute in the opening games but played against Bremen in Germany. We lost 4-0 but I thought I'd played quite well and was hopeful of being kept in the scheme of things. I was, because in the first few games of the season I was substitute."

BREAKTHROUGH!

"The game that really turned the corner for me was the 2nd leg of a 2nd round cup-tie against Stirling Albion at Parkhead. The aggregate score was 2-2 after ninety minutes. I came on as substitute for George McCluskey in extra time and scored twice as we hammered in four more goals. Since then the boss has given me an extended run in the first team, though a couple of times he's given me a rest. I can't thank my team-mates enough. Without them I wouldn't be scoring the goals. I'm only part of a team.

"In my short time as a footballer, I've been luckier than most and I just hope to continue to make the same progress. I love playing for Celtic, and want to win every trophy possible with them."

> Two of Scotland's greatest prospects for the future who are obviously dedicated to their profession. Scottish football can look forward to success upon success as long as players of the calibre and attitude of John MacDonald and Charlie Nicholas are coming through.

23

Kenny's no dummy – but he keeps one at home, dressed in his racing leathers!

One thing Kenny has never lacked is "drive" . . . even on the golf course!

AT THE CASTLE OF
KING KENNY

When Kenny switches from two wheels to four, he does it in style – while retaining the famous yellow and black livery.

Kenny's den, full of mementos of his racing career, where he can relax with a game of table tennis.

The record books show that Kenny Roberts is America's greatest-ever all-round biker. He's only the second rider to have won all five forms of American bike racing in one year, his twenty-ninth U.S. national victory was a new record and, of course, there are his consecutive World 500 cc championship crowns on the European circuits.

But there's much more to Kenny than merely being a marvel on a machine. He refuses to side-step issues that affect his profession, his fellow racers and the future of the sport. That means he's often an outspoken critic of the running of motor-cycling, whenever its standards fall below those he sets himself. He's battled for a fairer deal for all riders, not just the top stars like himself, which was why he was instrumental in trying to form a World Series to run in opposition to the world championship.

Kenny's own efforts are directed at securing a comfortable lifestyle for his family — and perhaps it's only when he returns home that he can fully relax. Away from the pressures of Grand Prix, Kenny enjoys golf, ski-ing and fishing — or merely lounging around in the comforts of his luxurious home in northern California.

He's certainly earned the right!

With skis replacing wheels, Kenny takes to the slopes.

Wheelie popping – the confident style of a World Champion at work.

JUMBO SPORTS

CLUES ACROSS

10. Willie Carson will use this to mount his horse (7)
11. A Building Society in the Fourth Division (7)
12. American speedway star, Bruce (7)
15. Lillieshall is an F. A. Coaching — (6)
16. Top striker with Tottenham (9)
17. Worth two points in billiards (6)
18. Phil Edmonds is famed for this kind of bowling (4)
20. One better than a birdie (5)
22. Bearded striker in his second spell with Charlton (5)
23. Top U.S. golfer, Jerry (4)
24. Many a weightlifter has done this to his teeth (7)
25. The — of Man is famous for its T. T. Racing.(4)
26. Some athletes take this to help give them energy (7)
27. What goalkeepers may suffer from if they're constantly picking the ball out of the net (4 + 5)
33. Neil McNab plays for them (8)
34. He's partnered Sherwood Stewart often in men's doubles (1 + 7)
35. One of Aberdeen's bright youngsters — Cooper (5)
36. Mr Reardon (3)
37. Alan Ball is manager of this team (9)
38. The Argentinian golfer — Chi Rodriguez (3)
39. A hat-trick (5 + 5)
41. Players think that referees often give these kind of decisions (3)
42. This catches up with most sportsmen (3)
45. A boxer does this in a sauna (6)
46. The greyhound "Mick The Miller" was definitely this (4 + 3)
47. A corner at Silverstone (8)
49. Penalty — (4)
51. Football managers are often — (5)
53. Snooker colour (3)
54. (see 41 down)
56. World Darts Champion in 1980 and 1981. (4 + 7)
57. Tommy Cavanagh is the — — — (3 + 3 + 5)

CLUES DOWN

1. George Best once played for this team from the Fourth Division (9)
2. Wark, Souness and Strachan are a fine midfield — (4)
3. 56 across has scored many of these (9)
4. John Bond's team (10 + 4)
5 + 6. Two forwards who played for Brazil in the world cup triumphs in 1958 and 1962 (4 + 4)
7. The Magpies (9)
8. A guard protects it (4)
9. Athletes often have to undergo this examination (5 + 4)
13. Arsenal's shows a cannon (5)
14. Clemence and Dalglish are — of the Kop (5)
19 + 46. They won the European Cup in 1979 and 1980 (10 + 6)
21. Sandown is the venue for this famous steeplechase staged during April (9 + 4 + 3)
22. Scoop has sponsored this type of car in the past (9)
23. These conditions are good for skiers and climbers (6 + 4)
27. Bad tempered ice-hockey players are put in this bin (3)
28. Shortened version of Liverpool's Lee (3)
29. Ben — loves playing golf in Britain (8)
30. Leicester play at Filbert — (6)
31. The full back — for touch (6)
32. Stops the race at speedway (3 + 5)
40. What all footballers fear (3 + 5)
41 + 54 across, Speedway's Great Dane (3 + 5)
43. — Thistle (7)
44. The — on tennis racket strings is vitally important (7)
47. What a manager might call a striker who has rarely scored a goal (3 + 3)
48. There are always large — at Wembley finals (6)
50. Mallory — hosts many fine motor-cycle race meetings (4)
51. Heard often on a golf course. (4)
52. A — goal is worth three points in Rugby Union (4)
55. A "lovely" soccer team from France (4)

THIS MAN RIDES FOR COVENTRY (SEE 41 DOWN AND 54 ACROSS).

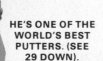

HE'S ONE OF THE WORLD'S BEST PUTTERS. (SEE 29 DOWN).

34 ACROSS IS A GREAT TENNIS TUTOR AS WELL AS A TOP PLAYER.

36 ACROSS IS ALWAYS AT THE END OF THE CUE.

CROSSWORD

ANSWERS ON PAGE 123

RECOGNISE THIS SCOTTISH STRIKER AND YOU'LL SOLVE 16 ACROSS.

THIS IS 56 ACROSS AIMING AT 3 DOWN.

27

Whatever the sport, real talent's worth watching. Here are some top stars I really rate,

Brian Jacks (signature)

DAVID GOWER

"Has emerged for me as the most exciting cricketer for several years. I've never met David, but have watched him with considerable interest and he's one of the few people that excites me when he goes to the wicket.

An hour of his magic, when it does come off, will always make up for any disappointments. He is again very much an individual. He is determined to succeed whatever, and he's certainly a young man with a great future in front of him, if the pressure of the media doesn't get to him. Somehow I don't think it will.

We do also have another thing in common, that is he took a body exerciser, my "Superjack" with him to the West Indies to assist in his training, so in a peculiar way I'm going to feel very much involved in his progress."

DAVID WILKIE

"David must rank as one of the greatest swimmers this country has ever produced. I've seen him swim a great deal and have spent many hours in the water with him.

For me, his elegance is one of his most outstanding features. The power and sleekness of his strokes make somebody like me feel totally out of place.

He's shown tremendous determination to succeed and has sacrificed a great deal to climb his own particular Everest, but he's changed very little. He's still the same smooth confident person, well-liked and respected by all age groups."

DALEY THOMPSON

"Rates in my book, and I'm sure in everybody else's, as the greatest all-round sportsman in the world. He has tremendous natural ability and dedication to his sport, and is one of the few people who very rarely change whether you see him competing or in the street. He's always got a wisecrack for everybody.

I certainly enjoyed my battles in the Superstars with Daley, though there was a noticeable contrast in the way we approached this competition and I was greatly relieved to have beaten him. But I don't think he'll ever let me forget his win in the weight-lifting.

I'm sure Daley will live up to all the expectations and with a bit of luck retain his Olympic title in Los Angeles."

CHRIS HUGHTON

"Team games aren't my favourites. Although appreciating the skills involved, I've always tended to prefer individualistic sports. That's one reason why Chris is one of my favourites.

He made an immediate impact on me when I first saw him play for Spurs. He just oozes with class. He's a tremendous two-footed player who appears to read the game well.

His skill on the ball and distribution is a pleasure to watch and he's always ready to come forward to have a crack at goal.

He's also got discipline, which is important in any sport. I understand from experts that he plays better on the right than on the left, but wherever he's asked to play he does his job without moaning. A real professional."

NEIL ADAMS

"Has to come into my top five. After all, Neil competes in my sport! He and I have known each other since he was 15 years of age, and in fact I was his trainer/coach for something like the first 2 years, and would hope that I've had an influence on his career to date.

Neil is a real loner who is hyped up on judo and winning. Off the mat he is quiet and reserved, on the mat he is a different animal, and only concerned with winning. He, like all top sportsmen, will need some luck in achieving his ultimate goal, and he is certainly the only person that I can see with the ability and dedication to win the First World and Olympic title for Britain in judo. After all, he's already an Olympic silver medallist!"

"NO-HOPER!"

GO on — shoot!"
Scrappy's cry rang in twelve-year-old Alan Gibson's ears as the ball skidded towards him across the wet grass. All he had to do was kick it and he'd surely beat the goalkeeper who was lying stranded on his line in front of him. But to trap the ball, or kick it first time? The scene took on a the quality of a slow-motion replay as his brain fumbled for an answer.

Then he wasn't quite sure what happened. But his cheeks were red and the ball was tumbling over and over high in the air above the crossbar to the groans of his team-mates.

"He always muffs it! Why did you pick him for our side, Scrappy?" someone complained.

"Because everybody else was picked, weren't they?" answered Scrappy. "He was the only one left."

The school bell clanged behind them for the end of lunchbreak and they all trooped through the gate connecting the football pitch and the playground. Alan brought up the rear, his head hanging, his cheeks burning with shame.

THE CHALLENGE

THE mis-kick haunted him throughout the afternoon and into the last-period history lesson. He'd intended trying a low drive but somehow or other his foot had disregarded his brain and gone right under the ball. He puzzled and puzzled why it should have happened, but the only satisfactory explanation he came up with was that he was an utter "no-hoper."

"Would you mind repeating what I just said about the Romans, Gibson?" Words filtered into his thoughts and, with a start he realised they were addressed to himself. Not only that, but Mr Marshall, his history master, was standing in the passageway beside him.

"They . . . they landed in 55 B.C.," he answered desperately.

"That was last week!" roared the teacher. "Write five hundred times 'I must not dream in class.' "

"He was dreaming about how not to play football," someone muttered, causing a ripple of laughter and adding to Alan's embarrassment.

It was a relief when the bell sounded at four o'clock. Outside he encountered Scrappy and his classmates from 1D having a raging argument with a group of 1C boys about football.

"My Granny knows more about football than you lot," scoffed Scrappy.

"Oh, yeh — maybe you *know* more about football," retorted Jack Forrest, a tall, broad lad from 1C, "but you can't *play* better'n us."

Alan stopped, his sympath-ies with Scrappy and his own classmates.

"Gibson's in 1D, isn't he?" said Forrest, suddenly aware of Alan's presence. They all whirled to look at him.

"So?" said Scrappy.

"Well, he's pretty repre-sentative, isn't he? Typical 1D standard."

"No, he ain't . . . he ain't." snarled Scrappy. "He's our worst player. He's picked last every time for a kick-about. He fluffs everything!"

"Like the rest of you," taunted the other boy to the chortles of his friends.

Alan was on the point of venturing some sort of defence when Scrappy spoke out for him.

"I mean, 'e's our worst player all right, but he's as good as any one of you lot . . . just needs experience and he'll reach the superior footballing standard of the rest of us."

"Whoo-hoo!" Forrest hooted with laughter. "Tell you what . . . we'll challenge you to a game tomorrow lunch-time. But Gibson must play too."

"Done!" Scrappy slammed his right fist into his open palm.

As the 1C lads raced off, jumping and slapping each other boisterously on the back, the enormity of what had happened settled over Scrappy and his friends like a black cloud.

"You shouldn't have done it," groaned Walter Apple-yard. "We could've beaten them. But not with Gibson in the team."

Scrappy ignored them and turned to Alan.

"You do your best tomorrow!" It was a mixture of a command and a plea. "We'll never live it down if they beat us!"

ALAN'S SECRET

AS he cycled homewards Alan was determined to practise more than usual that evening. Nobody knew about the secret practice ground he'd set up in the clearing in the wood behind his house. It had a ball dangling from a branch so that he could practise heading. A tyre hanging from another provided excellent shooting practice. Some evenings he kicked the ball through it with remarkable regularity.

There, away from prying eyes, he practised for hours at a time — low drives, lofted chips, body swerves, feinting, trapping, and ball control exercises, as they occurred to him.

But his favourite game was using the trees as opponents. With the ball glued to his foot, he dribbled and twisted around them, imagining all sorts of things — that he was playing for England or Manchester United, the first-year first eleven . . . or even just the fourth team.

He amazed himself at times with his ball skill. Some evenings he could almost make the ball sit up and beg.

The trouble was everything just disintegrated when he got on to a real football pitch.

Sometimes he wondered if he became so involved in his make-believe games that he imagined all the skilful things he did!

When he arrived home Mum had her coat on and Dad had just reversed the car out of the garage.

"Aunt Elsie has just moved into her new flat in town," Mum told him. "We're going over to see it. We'll have tea there."

"B . . . but, Mum, I want to practise football. And what about my lessons?"

"Take your books and your ball with you," said Dad, coming in the back door.

"He can't take his football," said Mum. "They don't approve of football outside those flats."

Alan argued — but Mum was unmoved. No football!

A slap-up tea at his aunt's failed to inspire his appetite. Nor could he concentrate on his lessons. The thought of the game to come made him sick.

The following morning his misery increased by the minute. His legs actually trembled when maths teacher Mr Pollock made him come to the blackboard to work out a sum.

Then the lunch-bell rang and there was no turning back.

Scrappy lead them on to the field as if he was a First World War commander taking his men over the top. Alan wished the ground would swallow him up or that he'd suddenly be transformed into another Pele.

To make matters worse, some of the younger teachers had heard of the challenge and had come to watch. Mr Law, who managed the first-year teams, had even agreed to referee, thus investing the game with an even greater importance.

1D won the toss and Scrappy tapped the ball smartly back to him. He almost tripped over it, but, to his relief, managed to slide it to Walter Appleyard, who set up an attack.

Alan had been ordered to play at inside-right, but he knew this didn't matter too much as everyone charged all over the place any old how. He decided to keep his nose clean and keep out of trouble. It seemed to work too. Although he mis-kicked occasionally, he didn't make any glaring mistakes.

Then came a corner at their opponents' end. He lost sight of the ball as he ran forward into the penalty area. He didn't see Scrappy trap the ball and release a

cannonball shot straight on target. SPHAT! — his head reeled, stars danced in front of his eyes. The ball bounced off the side of his head straight to a defender who cleared it straight back up the field.

"You clown! You got in the way!" Scrappy danced with rage.

But Alan didn't hear him. He was on his knees. His ears buzzed and everything wheeled blackly around him.

A friendly hand lifted him to his feet.

"All right, lad?"

"Oh, yes — fine, sir!" His ears had cleared slightly and he recognised Mr Law's voice.

A few moment later 1C scored to rousing cheers from their supporters. Alan didn't care, however. He was in a sort of light-headed daze and his fear had gone.

ALAN TURNS IT ON!

SHORTLY before half-time the ball landed at his feet. As he moved forward, still in a daze, a heavy, lumbering boy attempted to tackle him. But the ball seemed glued to his feet. He dribbled neatly past, laughing to himself. It was for all the world like playing around one of his trees.

Directly ahead on the eighteen-yard line, looking as solid as an oak, Jack Forrest blocked his path. But Alan saw that his legs were slightly apart. He hit the ball straight through and chased after it. Stupid, he thought, letting himself be "nut-megged" like that.

The keeper tried to block his shot. But Alan imagined a tyre dangling under the crossbar and kicked the ball through.

He blinked. The cheers of his classmates rang in his ears. He had equalised. One-all.

"A fluke!" grumbled Jack Forrest.

"Didn't know you had it in you," chortled Scrappy, slapping his back. "But Forrest is right — it must've been a fluke."

1C scored again immediately after half-time.

"Come on! We've got to get that goal back," shouted Scrappy.

1D put on the pressure. Walter Appleyard crossed from the left wing. In the middle of a scramble of players in front of the opposition's goal Alan felt the ball touch his foot. Back to the goal, he pivoted, drag-

ging the ball with him. He tapped it forward, jumped an outstretched leg — and hit it right on the button. The ball drove low and hard past the diving keeper, giving him no chance. Still in a daze, he heard his classmates cheering him again. It was two-all.

A tough battle followed. The play swung from end to end as time began to run out. In desperation the players realised that only ten minutes remained in which to determine the better team.

Alan headed a cross from the right wing. The ball slammed the 1C crossbar, leaving it vibrating.

"Hard luck!" Scrappy shouted in sympathy.

Alan shrugged. But the header had suddenly brought everything sharply into focus. His light-headedness disappeared.

Then, with three minutes left to play, he found himself chasing a loose ball in the centre of the 1C half.

"My ball, you no-hoper!" shouted Jack Forrest, racing toward it too, his lips curled in a snarl.

For a moment Alan's confidence ebbed. Then he reminded himself that he'd beaten Forrest before — and half the 1C team, too, if it came to that. He reached the ball first, jinked left then right, leaving Forrest swaying stupidly in the wrong direction and unable to turn quickly in pursuit.

He passed to Scrappy as another defender threatened him. The ball came back — hitting the ground directly in front of the 1C goal. Alan didn't hesitate. Leaning back slightly, he took it on the half-volley and hit it past the outstretched keeper's arms, a foot under the bar.

The final whistle blew and Scrappy ran forward and grabbed him by the shoulders. The pair danced around in delight to the congratulations of their team-mates.

"Well played, lad." Even Mr Law praised Ian.

"And he's our worst player," chortled Scrappy, catching sight of Jack Forrest's disgruntled features.

"I doubt that," replied the teacher.

The following week, to his amazement, Alan found his name down for the third team. By the end of the term he was playing regularly for the second team. He had lots of good games but never one quite as spectacular as that one. But the stage-fright — the lack of confidence — for that's what it was, was gone. He was never worried about playing football again.

31

The End

LIAM BRADY

" I love to score goals. I may be a midfield player whose job is to create, but there's still a tremendous thrill in putting the ball in the back of the net."

SPEED KINGS

Spectacular action from Ron "Speedy" Hutton, who, along with Greasy Tanner, forms the brilliant motor sport duo known as Speed Kings. Following successes at everything from karting to Grand Prix racing, Speed Kings are now at work in a film studio . . .

33

John, a friend from Ron's rallying days, takes them to his workshops . . .

Hi, lads, good to see you again! I'm here on business, and I want to show you a very special car. Can you spare half an hour?

Meet the Viper, lads — the rally car on which I've staked everything! My money, my workshops . . . everything!

WOW! She's a beaut, John!

The reason I asked you here is because I want you to return to rallying. But not just any rally, Ron — I want you to drive the Viper in the MONTE CARLO RALLY!

JEEPERS!

The Monte, eh? That's one we haven't tackled before, Greasy . . .

The Speed Kings agree, and the following days are spent route planning and testing . . .

Phew! Mile after mile through the Alps to Monte Carlo, with special stages all the way . . .

. . . then nine special speed stages, mostly at night on icy mountain roads, and all with a car that's never been tested!

She's a winner, Greasy!

No problems on tarmac either!

The next day, just as the service crews set off in advance . . .

See you in France — BLIMEY! WHAT WAS THAT —?

CRRASH

MAJORS

RALLY MUNIE CARLO

MAJORS

OH, NO! THE VIPER! LOOK AT IT! WHAT HAPPENED?

No idea! That metal rack just toppled over! One of the youngsters must have loaded it badly!

MAJORS

Oh, no! Not another set-back! Two weeks ago we had a mysterious fire! And before that, some spare parts went missing! We're jinxed I tell you!

Don't panic, John! It's just a few dents and scratches. We've still got two days to get the Viper roadworthy! Send the service teams on their way — we can fix her!

Two days later the British entrants converge on the south coast . . .

Reports are coming in of foul weather in the French Alps! The worst blizzards in years! Your reaction, Ron?

We've packed our dog sledge and huskies! We'll get through!

WE'RE OFF! Three thousand miles of driving in the worst conditions the weather and the rally officials can organise!

WE MUST BE MAD!

34

36

Two hours later . . .

WE'VE MADE IT, GREASY — MONTE CARLO!

Later . . .

A good time with only minimal penalty points. We're in sixth place, John!

Good going, but you're not finished yet! You've got plenty special night stages to come!

At that moment the second crew arrives . . .

What on earth happened to you, Arthurs? We needed a tyre change and repairs at St Apollinaire!

We had a puncture and our spare tyre was mysteriously mislaid by my partner! He says he loaded it, but . . .

Markku Airikkala is leading . . .

So, my English rivals. You are in good position. Only seconds separate you from the others . . . but I am a good minute ahead.

The way our car's performing even YOUR lead's not safe.

Ho-ho! We'll see.

Later . . .

Someone's in among the cars! Looks as if he could have been sniffing around the Viper! HOI!

He's running for it! Come on. You check the car — I'll catch him.

The man escapes Ron, but minutes later . . .

Whoever it was has done the brakes so they'll give after a few goes!

Our saboteur! Just as I thought! But who? HEY LOOK — IT'S ARTHURS!

This little man ran into me just after I leave you! I hear shouts . . .

Arthurs is forced to confess that he's in the pay of the Speed Kings rival Team Amco . . .

Amco may have a full size team in the race, but they've not done well for years! Their car's not up to it — they need new ideas!

And if they couldn't come up with them, they'd steal 'em, eh? I knew this was no jinx! Thanks for your help, Markku!

Markku's still nearly a minute ahead of us in time, Ron. I guess we've no chance of catching him now!

No — but he'll have to go full pelt just in case.

The guy in front has a dickie engine. He's blocking us! Holding us up! We were gaining every mile up to now, Ron!

Desperate situations call for desperate action! Hang on.

37

YIKES! SOME SHORT-CUT, RON!

Made it! Reckon we're clear in second place now — HEY! There's someone ahead. It's the Finn! He must have had a stoppage or he wouldn't be on the same part of the stage as us!

We've gained almost a minute on him!

Our times must be identical. We've only to beat him to the finish line to win, by my calculation! Let's go!

But at the very first opportunity . . .

With our change of tyres, we've now got the edge on him for speed! But there's no way past!

And no chance of squeezing through THESE trees!

WE'VE GOT HIM! STEP ON IT, RON.

WE'RE FLAT OUT! WE'VE GOT TWO BLOOMIN' WHEELS IN THE DITCH REMEMBER!

DONE IT! WE'RE THROUGH!!

When the times and penalty points are added up, the Speed Kings win is confirmed!

YAHOO! I RECKON WE'VE MADE IT!

That's some car you built, Majors. Next time I see someone try to sabotage it, I leave them to it, eh? Unless I am driving it, that is!

And why not mate!? Greasy and I will be movin' on now!

MOVING ON? BLIMEY — HAVEN'T YOU TWO HAD ENOUGH YET!?

THE END

38

TARGET TIME!

So you reckon you know your football, eh? Right — have a go at this quiz, and as the title suggests, the nearer the bull you get, the harder the questions become!

The twelve easy questions on the ORANGE outer ring are worth 5 POINTS EACH. The four slightly harder questions on the inner WHITE ring are worth 10 POINTS EACH, and the two questions in the BULL are worth 15 POINTS EACH! That's an overall total of 130 POINTS if you're bang on target!

1. If you were watching a game between Aris Salonika and Olympiakos, which country would you be in?

2. Who were runners-up in the 1980 European Championships in Italy?

3. Which North American club did Pele play for between 1975-1977?

4. Nikolai Jovanic has starred in many games for Manchester United. Which country does he play for?

5. Which club has a pie stall at Tannadice Park?

6. Do F.I.F.A. laws insist that a player must wear football boots or shoes?

7. St Mirren and St Johnstone are two famous Scottish clubs. Which one plays at Muirton Park?

8. Only one player has scored a hat-trick in a World Cup Final — who was he?

9. Where was the 1981 European Cup Final held?

10. Before joining Southampton, Dave Watson played for a German team. Was it Werder Bremen, Hertha Berlin or Dusseldorf?

11. Who or what is Vetch Field?

12. Liverpool have never been relegated. True or False?

13. One Football League club has a pair of seals in its club crest and is known as "The Seals." Which one?

14. If a player is ordered off before a match starts, after misconduct during the pre-match warm up, for example, can a substitute be played in his place?

15. They play in red, and they play at the Gzira Stadium — which international team are they?

16. What have football managers Frank O'Farrell, John Bond, Noel Cantwell, Ken Brown, Dave Sexton and Geoff Hurst got in common?

17. One of the current stars of the England squad was once loaned to Lincoln City, and then loaned to Doncaster Rovers, while signed for the club he later became famous with. Who is he?

18. The present F.A. Cup is the third trophy to be used in the competition. It was first played for in 1911, and the team that won it came from the same city in which it was made. Who are they?

NOW TURN TO ANSWERS ON PAGE 123

FRIENDS AND FOES!

Stan Cummins (signature)

SUNDERLAND'S STAN CUMMINS HAS HIS SAY

CRUNCHING tackles, no-holds-barred battles for possession, players being sent-off and booked, confrontation on the pitch—sometimes it seems that a game of football is one long battle. Some people get the impression that footballers are at daggers drawn with their opponents but on most occasions once the whistle blows for full-time most of the " aggro " goes too. There are the occasional " feuds " that are carried on from one game to another. But usually once the game's over most of the players are the best of pals.

DENNIS MORTIMER (ASTON VILLA)

GORDON COWANS (ASTON VILLA)

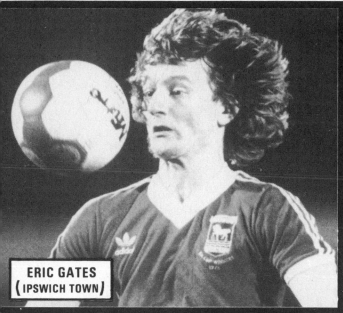

ERIC GATES
(IPSWICH TOWN)

KENNY
SANSOM
(ARSENAL
AND
ENGLAND)

That's what I've found. I've made quite a few friends from amongst players that I've played against. Kenny Sansom, the Arsenal full-back, is one. I met Kenny for the first time when we were in an England Under-21 squad and since then we've been pretty good pals. Not that that means that Kenny gives me an easy time of it when we're playing against one another. And I'm just as determined to do well against him.

Another lad I'm friendly with is Eric Gates of Ipswich. Eric comes from the same part of the world as me—Ferryhill in Co. Durham. We've also got one other thing in common—both of us are built a bit on the wee side! But despite his lack of inches Eric's had a lot to do with Ipswich's good run over the last season or two. Whenever Sunderland plays Ipswich Eric and I usually manage to have a chat after the game.

It's a local competition, too, that gives me something in common with Newcastle's David Barton. We know each other from our school days when we played against one another for our respective teams. But we also played in the same schoolboy team at County and district level. It's a while since we met on the pitch in a professional game, but I'm sure we'll have a real battle when we do meet.

Someone else with local connections that I'm friendly with is Gordon Cowans of Aston Villa. I really got to know Gordon when we were in the England Under-21 squad together. These sort of gatherings are great for getting to know your fellow professionals. Gordon has relatives in Ferryhill whom I know quite well. When we play Villa, Gordon's relatives usually turn up to watch and after the game we have a bit of a chat. It's usually pretty friendly, no matter who's won!

Apart from meeting Gordon I remember the games against Villa because of the displays of Dennis Mortimer. With Villa doing so well last season the team got a lot of publicity and deservedly so. But I think that Dennis's play often didn't get the publicity it should have done. He played brilliantly against us, and as team skipper I think he'd a lot to do with Villa's success. I know when we played against them Dennis was undoubtedly their best player.

Last season Sunderland didn't do as well as all of us at Roker Park had hoped and I'm sure it was a bit of a disappointment for our fans. But despite their disappointment they still gave us tremendous support. In fact they helped create the atmosphere for one of the real highlights of my football career. That was the Saturday that Sunderland played their fist game in the First Division after a gap of several seasons. The ground was packed, the atmosphere was tremendous—and we beat Everton 4-1. What more could you want!

I must say the fans have been tremendous to me since I joined Sunderland. That's why I'd like to put them at the top of the list of my friends in football.

THE TWO

The sports gear room— with rugby and footballs!

Back on September 14th, 1980, 9554 fans turned out to see Fulham achieve a tremendous 24-5 victory against Wigan at Craven Cottage! No, it wasn't some kind of record football score. The two teams facing each other were playing that other great ball-game, rugby league. It was a real gamble. It had cost money to set-up the Fulham side and if the gamble had failed, then it could've spelt trouble for the Stevenage Road club.

But they needn't have worried. The crowds rolled up, the team flourished and a lot of other football clubs suddenly began to take an interest in the game Eddie Waring had made famous! We sent a Scoop photographer along to shoot some pics of the two matchdays at Craven Cottage.

The Fulham rugby league team bus rolls up . . .

. . . and so do the fans.

Last minute preparations in the dressing-room . . .

. . . then on to the field.

Time to meet the opposition.

A sight soccer fans thought they'd never see at Craven Cottage!

Plenty of action to keep the fans happy.

And after a thrilling game, full time.

MATCHDAYS

And the following Saturday it was soccer's turn . . .

Talk-in with manager Malcolm MacDonald.

Last minute preparations . . .

. . . and out of the tunnel.

The toss of the coin . . .

. . . and into the action.

Malcolm MacDonald follows every move.

As the pace hots up, it's substitution time.

And Fulham keep up the pressure.

PS Fulham won both the matches. The soccer side saw Swindon off with a 2-0 scoreline and the rugby league side triumphed over Huyton with a 24-4 score-line!

THE MAESTRO WITH MAGIC IN HIS BOOTS

GREAT MOMENTS IN SPORT 1953

With twenty minutes of the 1953 F.A. Cup Final remaining, Blackpool were trailing Bolton Wanderers by three goals to one and seemingly destined to become runners-up for the third time in six seasons.

It was then that the wing wizardry of Stanley Matthews took over. England's international winger already had two loser's medals — he didn't want a hat-trick! Single handed, Matthews pulled Blackpool back into the game as he cut Bolton's left flank to shreds with the finest individual display ever witnessed on the Wembley turf.

Two goals brought the score to 3-3 and with the game moving into the last minute, Matthews cut his way down the touchline once again, leaving defenders gasping in his wake, centred . . . and there was Stan Mortensen waiting to clinch a famous victory for Blackpool.

While the record books show that Mortensen had become the first player ever to score a Cup Final hat-trick, the glory belonged to the maestro with magic in his boots. Even now, almost thirty years later, the match is known as "The Matthews Final". There hasn't been a performance to rival it!

Blackpool skipper Harry Johnston holds the cup — while Matthews is hoisted shoulder high by delighted team-mates.

Seconds remaining as Matthews cuts in and centres . . . .

. . . and Stan Mortensen slips the ball into the net for Blackpool's winning goal.

44

What a shot, Jimmy!

You bet, Frankie!

What a goal to break the record with Jimmy!

That would have gone in if Marsden had boarded up his goal!

Hold it, lads! Marsden's hurt!

He'll be okay, won't he?

I don't know, son. He took that shot of yours on the jaw.

Baypool go on to win 5-0 . . .

Five-nil, lads. That should make Mr Kelly happy.

He doesn't look it. Something's wrong.

In Sam Kelly's office . . .

I've got bad news, Jimmy Tommy Marsden is dead. He died on his way to hospital.

WHAT? OH, NO, BOSS! I CAN'T BELIEVE IT!

Sam takes Jimmy home . . .

I KILLED HIM, MR KELLY! I KILLED HIM!

It was an accident, Jimmy.

The next morning . . .

OH, NO!

SUNDAY POST

MILLION TO ONE CHANCE KILLS KEEPER

SUNDAY SPORT

GOALIE DIES AFTER CANNONBALL BLAST

SUNDAY REC CANNONBALL KILLER SHOT

Monday morning . . .

How does it feel this morning, Jimmy?

Leave me alone, fellers, will you?

BAYPOOL ROVERS
FOOTBALL LEAGUE
DIVISION ONE
WEDNESDAY 21 APRIL
KICK OFF 7·30 PM
V
MULLFIELD
CITY

The following Wednesday . . .

I don't feel like playing! You'd be better putting on someone else boss!

We need these points, Jimmy. Get out there and forget what happened last Saturday!

The match starts . . .

Yours, Jimmy!

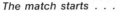

But Jimmy doesn't use his full power . . .

Jimmy's pulling his shots! It's like he's scared of hurting the goalie!

This Marsden business has really knocked the stuffing out of him.

City cash in on Jimmy's loss of form . . .

GOAL! 1-0 TO CITY!

In the second-half . . .

Cannonball passed when he could have burst the net!

And they've cleared it!

Baypool lose 1-0 . . .

LISTEN, JIMMY. YOU'VE GOT TO UNDERSTAND. TOMMY MARSDEN'S DEATH WAS AN ACCIDENT!

YES! AN ACCIDENT I CAUSED!

Next day . . .

We've got film of the Tommy Marsden incident Jimmy. I'd like you to see it.

Do me a favour, Mr Kelly. I don't want to see an action-replay!

I hope we get something out of this film, boss.

This is the shot. Now watch Marsden closely.

Jimmy shoots and Marsden raises his hands to cover.

But as the ball approaches he lowers his hands slightly.

Now look at that! The ball's gone right through between his hands.

The ball cracks him on the jaw, but he never got his hands to it at all.

So what does that prove, Mr Kelly? Could be that Marsden simply misjudged Jimmy's shot.

On Saturday Rovers play Akrington Albert . . .

Mr Kelly's right. I've got to snap out of it.

But . . .

COME ON, CANNONBALL! YOU CAN DO BETTER THAN THAT!

48

KENNY DALGLISH

"If I score or make a goal, and we win, that's it. I go home happy. If I score and we lose, I'm fed up."

And later . . .

THE KID MIGHT JUST AS WELL BE A SPECTATOR FOR ALL THE GOOD HE'S DOING LATELY!

The game ends in a 0-0 draw . . .

We had the Championship in the bag. Now we're going to blow it!

The following week Jimmy attends the inquest on Tommy Marsden . . .

The medical evidence shows that Mr Marsden died from a fracture of the skull.

But how could I have done that, Mr Kelly?

Tommy's father gives evidence . . .

Tommy had a slight accident the day before his death. His car had broken down and I was driving him to the ground for training.

"Tommy wasn't wearing his seat-belt . . ."

THE CRAZY FOOL!

OUCH! MY HEAD!

Tommy complained of a headache afterwards, but we didn't think much about it.

His skull was fractured in that accident. This was the real cause of his death.

That shot of mine had nothing to do with Tommy's death!

That's right, Jimmy. The film shows that Tommy was actually collapsing before your shot hit him

Jimmy feels a new man for Rovers final match of the season . . .

To win the Championship we've got to beat United by three clear goals!

Okay, boss!

Jimmy is soon in action . . .

GOAL!

THAT'LL DO FOR STARTERS!

But the Riverside United's goalie is no push-over . . .

But in the second-half . . .

GOAL! 2-0 TO BAYPOOL!

With minutes left . . .

NO! IT'S OUTSIDE THE BOX!

PENALTY!

Jimmy takes the free-kick . . .

GOAL!

The final whistle . . .

3-0! WE DID IT, JIMMY! THANKS TO YOU!

That was a bit too close for comfort, but we made it.

The End

ARENA SPECIAL

Darius Goodwin, Britain's seven-year-old stunt sensation, selects the sportsmen he'd leap through fire to see . . .

OLE OLSEN

I go to speedway at least once a week and it's my favourite sport. The most exciting riders to watch are Tony Briggs, Bobby Schwartz, Bruce Penhall, Peter Collins and Dennis Sigalos. But my favourite is Ole Olsen, and what I like about him is that he seems to win a lot of races from the back. Some riders are good at gating, but Ole is fantastic at passing. His control and balance and timing are perfect. Sometimes I wish I'd been born earlier because I'd liked to have watched Barry Briggs. My dad reckons he was the most exciting speedway rider of all time. I know that it's dangerous but it doesn't put me off, and though my mum doesn't fancy the idea, I can't wait till I'm old enough to have a go!

EDDIE KIDD

Everybody seems to think that Evel Knievel is my hero. In a way he is, because he's the greatest showman ever, in motorcycle jumping. But he's not the best jumper. I've got a lot of videotapes of his jumps, and he's not very consistent. And he used to crash a lot — I've heard that he's broken every bone in his body. My favourite jumper is Eddie Kidd — his style is great and so is his balance and control. I first met Eddie when I was only four years old. He invited me along to one of his practice sessions, and let me stand between his ramps as he jumped high over me. Eddie is fun to be with and he's been ever so helpful, giving me lots of tips on how to improve my own jumping.

My speedway favourite, Ole Olsen.

Eddie Kidd takes off – over me!

KEVIN KEEGAN

I love football — I play all the time. My favourite team is Arsenal and my favourite player is Kevin Keegan. He's such a busy little player and he seems to be everywhere at the same time. I like players with lots of energy. People tell me that Alan Ball was like that but I never saw him play. Kevin Keegan is great at scoring goals and he turns so quickly. He can run, too. More than any other footballer, I'd like to play like him.

Kevin Keegan – "a busy little player" – jousts with Liverpool's Phil Neal and Sammy Lee.

George Bailey crashes another car, but all his stunts are carefully planned.

J. P. R. WILLIAMS

I play rugby as well as football and I like it a lot — especially when the ground is wet and muddy because you don't get so many bruises when somebody trips you up! The best player I've seen (but only on the telly) is J. P. R. Williams. He seems to be the "King" of rugby — everybody talks about him. I like the way he catches the ball — it's always safe in his hands and he never drops it. I read in a magazine that J. P. R. is a doctor and that surprised me because doctors have to look after their hands and rugby is a pretty rough game.

GEORGE BAILEY

Motorcycle jumping will always be my favourite stunt, but when I grow up, I'm going to be an all-round stunt man. People say that I'm too young to be really sure what I'm going to do when I'm older, but they're wrong. I'm going to be a stunt man . . . just you wait and see. It's an exciting thing to do and I'll be able to go to lots of other countries and meet people. The best stunt man is my friend George Bailey, who is teaching me a lot of tricks. You've probably seen George in lots of films, but you wouldn't recognise him because he 'doubles' for other people. George does all sorts of stunts in cars, on motorcycles and horses, water stunts, everything. He's best at jumping out of high buildings and helicopters. It's very dangerous, but he takes a lot of time preparing a stunt and leaves nothing to chance. George says that the secret is careful planning, confidence and fitness, and I know he's right because he's the best.

J. P. R. WILLIAMS

ALEX HIGGINS

Snooker is a smashing game. I watch it whenever I can on telly. Sometimes I go with my dad to his club on Saturday mornings. I'm not allowed on the big snooker tables yet, so I play pool, which is the same sort of game. I stand on an empty milk crate so that I can line up my shots properly. My favourite is "Hurricane" Higgins. He's different from all the other snooker players — very fast but very accurate. He must have marvellous eyesight. And I like the way he plays trick shots to please the audience. He's a real showman and I really want him to be World Champion again, because he's the best.

SIMON WIGG

ALEX HIGGINS

SIMON WIGG

Grass track racing is a bit like speedway, except that the tracks are much bigger and the surface is grass instead of shale. The bikes aren't much different except that they have gear boxes on grass. It's very fast, and it's a terrible strain on your arms because you have to get your wheels out of line to broadside round the turns. My favourite rider is Simon Wigg and he deserves to be British Champion. He also rides speedway and he and Tony Briggs are teaching me. I have my own speedway bike, with no brakes, which was made for me by Barry Briggs, who was world speedway champion four times. It scares me a bit because it's so fast, but with Simon and Tony to teach me the right things, I'll be OK. When I'm older, I'd like to do a bit of racing . . . grass, speedway, road racing, all sorts.

ONE THING THAT REALLY GETS ME HOPPING IS MY DAD TACKLING A 'SPOT THE BALL' COMPETITION. I'M ALWAYS SURE I CAN DO IT BETTER THAN HIM—BUT HE NEVER GIVES ME THE CHANCE! SO, FOR THE BENEFIT OF ALL YOU READERS IN A SIMILAR POSITION, HERE'S YOUR VERY OWN . . .

Just study the football action pictures shown below and decide which square you think the ball should be in. I've left a space for three tries at the side of each picture.

Aston Villa's Peter Withe looks to have won this aerial duel—but has he?

Derek Parkin *could* have his eye on the ball in this Wolves/Watford clash.

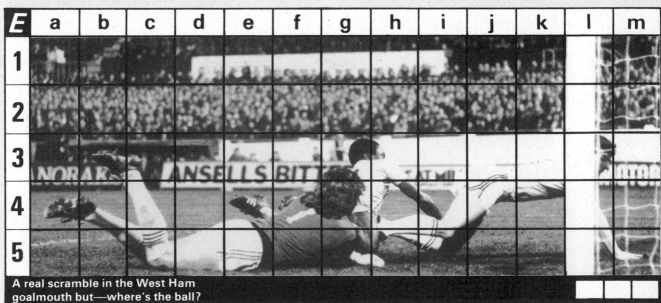

A real scramble in the West Ham goalmouth but—where's the ball?

SPOT the BALL COMPETITION

COMPLIMENTS OF BALLBOY FROM 'THE BEANO'!

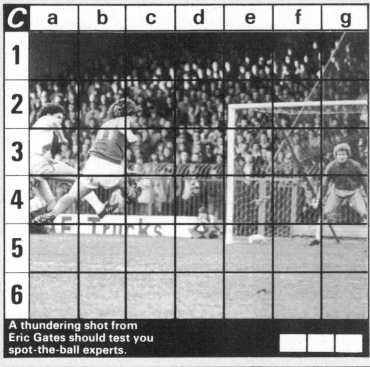

C

	a	b	c	d	e	f	g
1							
2							
3							
4							
5							
6							

A thundering shot from Eric Gates should test you spot-the-ball experts.

D

	a	b	c	d	e
1					
2					
3					
4					
5					
6					

Villa on the run for Spurs with Steve Williams of Southampton looking on.

F

	a	b	c	d	e	f	g
1							
2							
3							
4							
5							
6							

High-flying action from West Brom's Cyrille Regis.

G

	a	b
1		
2		
3		
4		
5		
6		

Well, I hope you haven't had too much trouble spotting where the balls might be, but if you have—here's one you can't possibly get wrong!

Answers ON PAGE 123

55

Giants of the fairway

Jack Nicklaus holds the record for the longest drive in the U.S.P.G.A. – 341 yards at sea level.

Sevvy Ballesteros, in the 1978 Hennessy Cup at the Belfry, drove the 310-yard 10th hole. The hole was specially designed with tall trees and water guarding the green so it couldn't be driven . . .

At thirteen years old Jack Nicklaus shot a scratch 69 at Scioto, a 7095-yard championship course.

Jack Nicklaus after winning his first "major," the U.S. Open in 1962, "I want to be the best golfer the world has ever seen . . ."

American Ed Fiori speaking about Ballesteros's leading margin after third round of the 1980 Masters. "He'll have to break a leg — and even then that might not stop him!"

Nicklaus on Ballesteros: "He's the best young player to come along in a long, long time. If anyone is to equal my majors record, Ballesteros appears to be the most likely candidate."

Ballesteros on Nicklaus: "He has great talent as everybody knows. He thinks very positively and he has a great presence, and that is very important. He also has all the power and spirit."

Right: A winning smile from Jack after capturing the British Open title at St Andrews in 1978.
Second right: The concentration that makes a champion is shown in Jack's face as he powers a tee-shot away.

JACK NICKLAUS is well built, blond and is obviously of Germanic descendancy. Severiano Ballesteros is tall, slim, raven haired and totally Latin. "Chalk and cheese" to use a proverbial descriptive phrase. However, these two greats of golf do have something in common — power!

The way they make contact with a golf ball, par fives are often reduced to "pitch and putt" proportions. There are of course many professionals who can launch fairway missiles, but the difference between them and Nicklaus and Ballesteros is the latter two are "winners." Not only do they hit the ball a long way, the rest of their game is brilliant too. Sevvy Ballesteros is one of the best putters in the world and it's doubtful if there is a better sand-iron player from just off the green than Jack Nicklaus.

Nicklaus is of course much older than Sevvy. Indeed when Jack was winning his first U.S. Open in 1962, the young Spaniard was just starting school.

Both players were sensational teenagers. Sevvy burst on to the scene in 1976 when, as a nineteen-year-old, he finished joint runner-up to Johnny Miller in the British Open at Muirfield. Likewise, Jack was only nineteen when he won the U.S. Amateur Championship in 1959. A year later, whilst still an amateur, he finished second to the legendary Arnold Palmer in the U.S. Open with a four-round total of 282. The lowest-ever score recorded by an amateur in that tournament.

Since then Jack Nicklaus has re-written the golf history books. He is the best golfer of all time. Before the past season he had won 17 "majors" (the U.S. Open, U.S.P.G.A., the Masters and the British Open). A total which looks to be unsurpassable – unless of course your name happens to be Severiano Ballesteros. He is the only player good enough and young enough to perhaps catch the Golden Bear. His Open win at Royal Lytham in 1979 and his Masters win in 1980 shows he has the temperament to match the skill required to win a major tournament.

Jack Nicklaus's record undoubtedly makes him King of the fairways but he has an heir in Prince Severiano. Time will tell if the Prince can take over from the King.

Left: Sevvy gives a victory salute after winning his first major – the British Open at Royal Lytham in 1979.
Second left: Sevvy demonstrates the putting stroke that is the envy of many a pro golfer.

"SPAIN – I'D LOVE TO BE THERE!"

Says
GLENN HODDLE

GLENN HODDLE

Twenty-four teams go into the Spanish sombrero in January for the draw for the 1982 World Cup finals.

I would give almost anything to be actively involved in the World Cup finals.

It must be the ambition of any professional footballer to take part in the final stages of the most important competition in the game.

Compared to the 1978 competition there are eight more teams included in the finals and if you want to be considered world class you have to be taking part.

The last couple of years have been devoted to the qualifying rounds and the build-up and I can tell you that even the group matches of the World Cup have an atmosphere of their own.

A lot of very good players in England have never played in the World Cup finals. We have not qualified since the 1970 competition in Mexico, so none of the current England squad has experience of the finals.

Players who completed their international careers in the '70s—like Roy McFarland (28 caps), Mike Channon (44 caps) and Martin Chivers (24)—all missed out on World Cup finals.

I'd hate to go through my career and miss out at the highest level. To actually win the World Cup must be an unbelievable feeling. It takes a special blend of skill, experience and stamina to pace yourself through a tournament like the World Cup finals.

We had a taste of it at the European Championships last year. That was on a minor scale compared to the World Cup but I learned a lot that I hope will stand me in good stead in the future.

Quite apart from lessons on technique and tactics that you pick up from playing against and watching foreign sides, there are things to learn from living together in a squad for two or three weeks or more.

Being away from home and living out of suitcases is nothing new for a footballer. There are always trips and tours taking place.

But coping with tournament tensions when you are in this sort of situation takes a bit of getting used to.

I usually room with Kenny Sansom of Arsenal on England trips. We shared a room in Italy last year and got on well, as we have known each other since playing for the England Youth side.

I took my cassette player and we spent a lot of time listening to tapes together, or just talking football.

Boredom is a big danger when you are away from home. If you are stuck in a hotel with nothing to do after training but laze around, that lethargy can stay with you when you go out to play.

I learned last year to have plenty of things to do to avoid the problem—like car games, books, tapes, and a tennis racket for the occasional game.

DIEGO MARADONA

I also try to stick to exactly the same routine in foreign games as I follow for a normal Spurs match.

The same mid-day meal—steak or chicken—and tea and toast around 5 o'clock for an evening match, with a sleep in the afternoon.

Looking ahead to the 1982 finals, it's going to be a fiesta of football. With so many teams taking part it's even harder to try to forecast the likely winners.

For once I think the South American teams may do well in Europe—where they have not flourished since Brazil's win in Sweden in 1958.

The location in Spain will suit them. For one thing the Argentinians will be able to speak the language and that gives them a definite advantage.

They have made several trips to Europe in recent years and should know all about the playing conditions. With players like Diego Maradona they've also got the skill to hold on to their World Champion tag.

The Argentinians have also had several players performing in Europe at club level—like Mario Kempes (Valencia) and my spurs team-mate Ossie Ardiles—and that kind of experience will be valuable.

From what I've seen on television, Brazil could be a big danger again. They look to me to have their most skilful side since the 1970 winning team of Pele, Gerson, Rivelino and company.

Even when they lacked that kind of flair the Brazilians still got to the 1974 semi-final, and finished third in 1978.

Looking at them now they seem to resemble the '70 side in individual skill, and with their tradition that must make them one of the favourites.

Naturally, Spain, the host country, must figure among the contenders. With support from their own crowds the home country nearly always does well in the World Cup. They have had time in the last few years to build up to the finals.

Spain has always produced good individual players and with time to make the blend they will be dangerous.

Nobody would rule out the West Germans either. As they proved in Italy last year they can produce great players from nowhere—like Bernd Schuster—and fit them into the team without disruption.

The West Germans must rank as one of the most consistent international sides in the world. They produce skilled footballers with good technique, who are also very strong and fit.

They seem to have the knack of being able to pace themselves through a tournament. This is very important. They do just enough to get through the early matches, saving something for later.

With so many teams qualifying for Spain there will probably be more surprises than ever, so it's difficult to predict what will happen next summer in Spain.

All I know is it will be a great occasion for football and footballers—and I'd love to be there.

MARIO KEMPES

BERND SCHUSTER

COMO

LT ... THE TEAM THAT CA$H BUILT...

"MONEY CAN'T BUY SUCCESS" — that's an expression which is often too true when associated with football. Look at British big spenders Manchester United, Everton, Tottenham and Manchester City — they haven't exactly dominated domestic silverware over the last few years. Maybe it's because they've always been able to afford a few big-name players, but buying a *complete* team of superstars has never been possible. Nor has any top European club ever "bought" a side. But there is one team made up of stars, and in their case, money really has bought success!

NEW YORK COSMOS first rose to prominence 'way back in the early days of North American soccer when they won the 1972 N.A.S.L. Championship, but it wasn't until 1977 that they re-emerged, like a slumbering giant, to prominence —— backed by the massively wealthy film corporation, Warner Brothers.

Cosmos started off their second life as they meant to continue . . . the best in America! They wanted success and weren't prepared to wait for any coach to produce it from a long term youth policy. The Cosmos bosses looked on football as a business, not a sport. As far as they were concerned, anything and anybody could be bought.

So, in 1975, when they decided that a "personality" player was needed to take the crowds away from baseball, and grid iron football, cash was made available . . . and since the Cosmos bosses were used to style, they made their first big signing in style — they bought Pele!

Make no mistake about it — the thing which took Pele to New York was MONEY. Of course, the great man had always wanted to be one of the first to introduce soccer to the States, but it was a huge and lucrative contract worth nearly two million pounds which finally took him north from his Brazil homeland.

A RASH OF CASH

Franz Beckenbauer was the next soccer legend to pull on the white of Cosmos, and again it took a contract reputedly worth nearly £2,000,000. Brazilian World Cup winning captain Carlos Alberto was also recruited and was closely followed by his albino blond countryman Francisco Marinho. Like the rest, Marinho was persuaded by a flashy car, a fancy house, and enough dollars to fill quite a few of the bongo drums which his country is famous for!

Pele, Alberto, Marinho and Beckenbauer — and add to them forty-seven-times capped Yugoslav internationalist Vladislav Bogicevic, and also the player who has turned out to be possibly their greatest-ever servant, Giorgio Chinaglia. After being released by Swansea City on a free transfer — definitely a case of "the one that got away" — Chinaglia became a goalscoring legend with F.C. Lazio, helping them to their first Italian Championship for years. Chinaglia reputedly earned £75,000 in his last year with the Rome team so

FRANZ BECKENBAUER — Kaiser Franz turned down the chance to play for West Germany in the 1978 World Cup to enable him to continue playing for Cosmos.

PELE — A contract worth millions of dollars

DENNIS TUEART

FRANCOIS VAN DER ELST
—Bustling action from one of Cosmos' newest and most expensive signings

it's not hard to imagine that once again Cosmos were not going to put a trifling thing like money between them and the player they wanted. Chinaglia was soon to pull on the No. 9 shirt for Cosmos!

And the big signings didn't stop. A big fee took our own Dennis Tueart to New York, and after failing to woo Johann Cruyff, a £750,000 contract was quickly drawn up to accomodate the other "Dutch Master" Johann Neeskens. World Cup team-mate Wim Rijsbergen wasn't slow in joining his countryman.

A NEW ERA

So, Cosmos already had a team of big-name winners as they moved towards the end of the 1970s. But the Dennis Tueart signing was the start of a new era of foreign Cosmos players, since he was the first big star to be bought while still in his soccer prime.

This new trend has continued, and the success of Cosmos on the field, both at home and on foreign tours, has swiftly turned them into a genuine world-class team rather than a travelling show of ageing stars. In 1980 they re-affirmed their desire to stay at the top by signing Julio Cesar Romero, voted the second best player in South America after Diego Maradona. The cheque book came out again for Belgian's Francois Van Der Elst, a tried and tested goalscorer even in the very best of European company.

That Cosmos will continue to dominate soccer in the United States is as certain as predicting Liverpool to continue at the top in England. In both cases the future looks rosy. But while Liverpool's success is based on the odd big-money signing backed up by good youngsters and good coaching, it looks as if future Cosmos successes will be built upon the buying power of the dollar.

They're still very much the Team That Cash Built!

JULIO CESAR ROMERO— The famous Giants Stadium scoreboard proclaims the arrival of yet another big signing.

GEORGIO CHINAGLIA—A magnificent record of goal-scoring since he joined Cosmos in 1977.

61

GENTLEMAN JIM

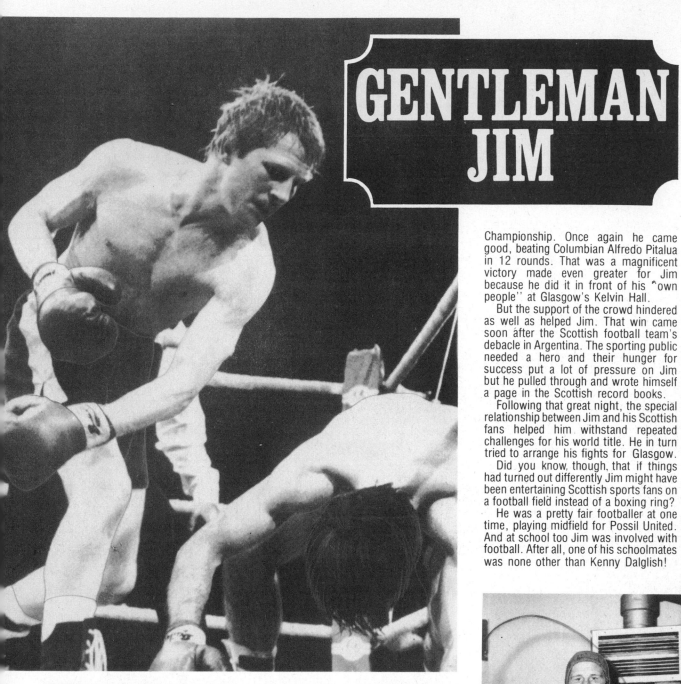

Championship. Once again he came good, beating Columbian Alfredo Pitalua in 12 rounds. That was a magnificent victory made even greater for Jim because he did it in front of his "own people" at Glasgow's Kelvin Hall.

But the support of the crowd hindered as well as helped Jim. That win came soon after the Scottish football team's debacle in Argentina. The sporting public needed a hero and their hunger for success put a lot of pressure on Jim but he pulled through and wrote himself a page in the Scottish record books.

Following that great night, the special relationship between Jim and his Scottish fans helped him withstand repeated challenges for his world title. He in turn tried to arrange his fights for Glasgow.

Did you know, though, that if things had turned out differently Jim might have been entertaining Scottish sports fans on a football field instead of a boxing ring?

He was a pretty fair footballer at one time, playing midfield for Possil United. And at school too Jim was involved with football. After all, one of his schoolmates was none other than Kenny Dalglish!

SUPER Scot Jim Watt isn't your run-of-the-mill boxer. For two reasons. First, he stands unchallenged as one of the most successful boxers in history. Second, he could never be accused of being the typical inarticulate fighter many people have come to expect in the fight game.

Even in the excitement following another championship win, Jim talks boxing as well as he fights it. Even with the pressures of Press and TV that all top sportsmen have to face nowadays, the likeable Scotsman is always Gentleman Jim.

But he didn't always look a champion. A few years back, Jim had paid his dues as a boxer. He'd learned his craft, proved he could take the punishment and that he could dish it out too.

Nothing though made Jim stand out from lots of other boxers. He needed an extra spark to turn him into a real champion, and that spark came when he signed up with London manager Terry Lawless.

The change was dramatic. Before then, Jim had won and lost the British light-weight title — though he won it again after fellow Scot Ken Buchanan retired. He'd also lost to Jonathan Dele in Lagos for the Commonwealth title and then to Andre Holyk in Lyons in a final eliminator for the European Championship.

Under Lawless though came consistent success. Jim won the Lonsdale Belt outright by beating Johnny Claydon and in 1977 took another major step in his career by stopping Andre Holyk in the first round — to become European Champion.

In April 1979 came the final challenge for Jim — the World Lightweight

YES – THE GREATEST

GREAT MOMENTS IN SPORT 1964

It was supposed to be the night that the Louisville Lip was going to be shut once and for all. Cassius Clay, ex-Olympic Light Heavy-weight champion, had pranced, danced and talked his way to a shot at the Heavy-weight Championship of the World.

Despite an undefeated record and a talent for bad poetry in which he forecast the round in which his opponent would be stopped, "Cass the Gas" was going to run out of steam that February night in 1964 — or so many fight fans thought.

Against him was Sonny Liston, the mauler who had brought mayhem and destruction to all his opponents in becoming champion. Nicknamed "The Bear" by Clay in the pre-fight build-up, Liston had to be restrained from starting the fight at the weigh-in. The scene was set for a holocaust!

But when the bell rang, Liston was never able to get to grips with his young opponent who "floated like a butterfly, stung like a bee."

At the end of the sixth round, the then battered, bruised body of the champion slumped down on its corner stool — and stayed there! Cassius Clay was the new Heavy-weight Champion of the World!

The legend of Cassius Clay, shortly afterwards to become Muhammad Ali, was born . . . and heavy-weight boxing was never to be quite the same again.

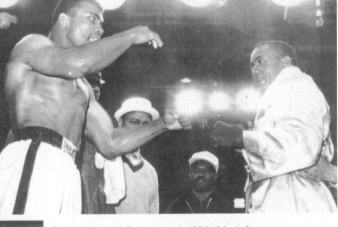

The big fight weigh-in — and Liston has to be restrained as Clay taunts and torments him.

The sixth and final round. With his left eye cut and swelling, Liston makes a last desperate attempt to salvage his title.

Seconds later it's all over — Cassius Clay is Heavy-weight Champion of the World!

BILLY BEAUMONT

"The little fast fellows at the back reckon they're the thoroughbreds and that the forwards like me are the donkeys. We're the ones you see in the messy, exciting bit—the scrum."

MAKING A SPLASH!

Slaloms, sprints, marathons—it sounds like a cross between skiing and athletics. But this is CANOEING!

It's all about balance and skill—and getting wet. Whether you're battling through white water on that slalom, or breathless in a arm-aching sprint, it's a sport which abounds in excitement.

Just look at these white water wonders!

THE JONES BOY

No-one had ever doubted Alan Jones' ability, but up to the start of the 1979 Formula One season, the Australian had only one GP victory to his credit. All he really needed was the right car—and that year he got it. By the end of the season, Alan's Saudia-Williams was dominating the sport and, in 1980, Alan's winning streak brought him the World Drivers' Championship.

Forceful, calculating and intelligent, Alan first came to this country in 1970 to race in Formula 3, having previously won the Australian Karting Championship. It's been a long road to the top—but it looks as if he's set to stay there for a long time.

The smile of a world champion— Alan Jones.

The "machine" that brought Alan success— the Williams FW07.

66

ALEX McLEISH SAYS "YOU MUST HAVE AMBITION"

ALEX McLEISH is one of Aberdeen's star players and an established internationalist for Scotland.

At 22-years of age he's achieved more in his five-and-a-half year career than many fellow professionals do in a lifetime. Many young players in a similar situation, have let success go to their heads but Alex has kept his feet on the ground, and speaks words of wisdom which one would expect from a player in the twilight years of his career, far less somebody of such a young age.

"Right from the start of my life in football, I've had the good fortune to be guided by the right people. My dad was and still is a tremendous influence on me. You know, he travels from Glasgow to see me play every week.

"Naturally, the various managers I've played under, have all played a major part in my climb up the ladder. From Teddy Scott, reserve team-coach, when I was starting out, to Ally McLeod, Billy McNeill and Alec Ferguson.

"They've all given me the benefit of their vast experience and I've learned a lot from them.

"However, if it hadn't been for a certain, special man way back in 1976, I might never have signed for the Dons. That man was Bobby Calder. He is the talent scout for Aberdeen on the west coast. He has been responsible for bringing players like Martin Buchan, Tommy Craig, Jimmy Smith, Willie Miller to Pittodrie—and the list of players could go on and on. I'll never forget the night he called to my mum and dad's house in Barrhead. I was playing for an under-18 Juvenile team, Glasgow United, at the time, and Bobby said he'd been watching me. He reckoned I could go far in football and Aberdeen wanted to sign me. He was a real charmer was Bobby. He gave my mum a box of chocolates and I remember him giving my little brother some money for sweets too. My mum thought he was a really nice man and if he was typical of Aberdeen F.C. I couldn't do any better than sign for them. My dad said it would be okay for me to go and in the summer of that year I was on my way to the Dons.

"Ally McLeod was manager and being a youngster I started on the ground staff. You've got to clean boots, baths and do other non-football tasks but I feel it teaches discipline and prevents you from being carried away with the idea of being a professional footballer. However, it was great to train with the star players, players I'd only seen on TV before.

"I spent most of my time in the reserve side under Ally McLeod, but when Billy McNeill arrived I was included in a few first team squads.

"My debut for Aberdeen is one of my proudest moments in football. It was on the 2nd January, 1977 against Dundee United. I was nervous, obviously, but after the whistle blew I soon settled down, I played quite well and the icing on the cake—we won 1-0!

"After the match, Billy McNeill called me into his office and told me that although I'd done a good job, he was leaving me out for the next week. It was no reflection on my play but he wanted to blood me slowly into the team. Naturally I was disappointed, but more importantly I accepted and understood his reasons. Billy McNeill, possibly because he was a centre-half too, spent a fair bit of time on me, and I'm sure it's had a good effect on my general play.

"The next season, I became something of a regular in the side and with each game I learnt a little bit more. As I look back, I consider myself fortunate but you've got to have faith in your own ability.

"For instance, playing for Scotland for the first time was very nerve-wracking but Jock Stein told me I was there on merit and just to play my usual game. It's a fantastic feeling to represent your country. Now that I've gained that honour, my ambition is to dominate the centre-half position in the Scotland team by making it my own. You must have professional ambition.

"Outside football, I've always taken a keen interest in accountancy. Some day I'd like to qualify as an accountant and set up my own business but that's quite a few years off yet. I've still got ambitions to achieve in football and they come first."

Alex McLeish is a great footballer and he's as great off the park as he is on it. He is a credit to his profession and an excellent model for any young player coming into the game to copy.

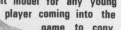

ALEX McLEISH, ABERDEEN & SCOTLAND

THEY GOT THE DROP ON ME!

"**H**I — my name's Norman, and if you read the 1981 "Scoop" Annual you'll know that the lads in the Scoop office have a habit of sending me away to have a go at unusual or exciting sports. On that occasion I nearly suffered frostbite while trying to learn windsurfing in December! Recently, John Thomson of Bristol wrote in challenging one of the staff to make a parachute jump. Who got the job? Why, the office mug — ME!!"

On arrival at Strathallan Airfield I discovered that another 12 "beginners" had decided to take the course. That made 13 in all! EEK!! Anyway, the first hour and a half were spent filling in forms and learning what we were going to be doing in the eight or nine hours of concentrated training . . .

Now, what's this one for? Aah – it enrols me in the British Parachute Association!

Later, two instructors gave us our first close-up look at a parachute. Bill Allen (left) and Frank Davies have made hundreds of jumps between them, and are Grade 10 instructors – that's the best you get!

You'll be using static lines which open your 'chutes automatically as you leave the aircraft. Right, Bill — walk a couple of steps forward . . .

As you jump, the static line opens the pack and your 'chute deploys. Only experienced jumpers are allowed to use ripcords.

Everyone got a grip of the 'chute? Okay, take a look at the way it's sewn together in panels, and made of rip-stop nylon. There's not much chance of any holes appearing as you're on your way down!

Bill Allen then taught us the static line jump exit procedure – one of the most important parts of our training . . .

ONE THOUSAND, TWO THOUSAND, THREE THOUSAND, FOUR THOUSAND — CHECK CANOPY!

Heads back and arms and legs apart! You've got to form an arc as you exit to ensure that you're in a stable upright position when your canopy opens!

Then it was back to the caravan for more theory. Use of the emergency parachute, wind directions, safety procedures, how to steer – we'd a lot to get through!

Cor! There's a lot more to this than meets the eye!

At all parachute bases, safety checks are very strict . . .

VISITING JUMPERS

A KIT CHECK IS IN FORCE AT THIS DZ IF YOU CANNOT PROVE DATE OF LAST RESERVE REPACK

IT WILL BE OPENED

Then, outside . . .

Okay, everyone, get into your gear! You're about to learn all about Parachute Landing Falls!

Oh-oh! This sounds painful!

And so . . .

Your elbows are still too far out! The force of your landing should be taken only on your feet, thighs and round part of your shoulder.

That's better — good roll!

By the time we'd practised landing falls for half-an-hour, I had bruises on top of bruises!

That's much better! Remember you've got six different positions for a P.L.F. — left, right, front left, front right, back left and back right. It all depends on which way you're approaching the ground.

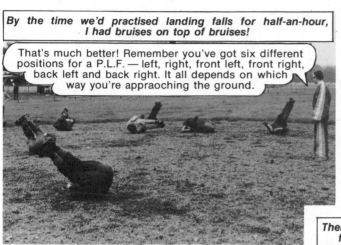

Next came more landing falls – but from a ramp this time, and at the run!

GERONIMO!!

Meanwhile, one or two other people were "dropping in" . . .

Then came our first close look at the aircraft we'd be jumping from – if we all came through our training okay . . .

Each one of us had to learn our exit position . . .

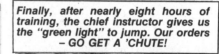

That's it! One hand on the floor and one on the side of the door. You don't just drop out of the plane. You've got to push yourself out and immediately start your exit count. Okay — give it a try . . .

And so . . .

ONE THOUSAND, TWO THOUSAND, THREE THOUSAND, FOUR THOUSAND — CHECK CANOPY!

Finally, after nearly eight hours of training, the chief instructor gives us the "green light" to jump. Our orders – GO GET A 'CHUTE!

At last! And the weather's great for jumping! Hardly any wind at all!

Will the SCOOP star go through with it? Turn to Pages 124 and 125.

"YOU'RE ALL

SWINGING — Jack Nicklaus and me. I'm the one in the red jersey!!!

"AND it's Pat Jennings in Car No. 4 in the lead" — that's not an announcement likely to be made at Brands Hatch, but it's one that I'd like to hear.

You see, one thing I would like to do is take part in Saloon Car Racing. I've seen quite a bit of it on TV, and it certainly appeals to me. However, there are one or two problems I'd have to overcome before I could get on to that starting line. For one thing I'd have to find someone daft enough to provide a suitable car. Then I'd have to get permission first from my wife — and second from Terry Neill. I don't know if the Arsenal manager would be too pleased if he was watching television one Saturday and saw a car come bombing round a corner, then career across the track and fling yours truly out through the windscreen on to the track!

That's one sport I've always wanted to try — but being a professional footballer can be a bit restricting. Obviously you

RIGHT, JACK!"

Says PAT JENNINGS

IF ONLY . . . the sort of scene I'd like to be part of.

have to avoid sports that could bring a risk of injury, or those that require some kind of specialist training. For instance, weight-lifting would be good for building up all-round strength which might be handy if they wanted the goal posts lifted and moved! But I doubt if it would improve agility very much — and this is the keystone of any 'keeper's fitness.

I like to watch most sports but golf is the only one that I play. I wouldn't say that Nicklaus and Ballesteros should have any sleepless nights worrying about any challenge from me — but it makes a fine break from football. I've watched one or two big tournaments at Wentworth, but I don't know if it's very good as far as building up any confidence is concerned. When you see the way the top pros perform it sometimes seems to be a totally different game from the one I play!

It's a golfer, in fact, who is one of my favourite sportsmen and that's Jack Nicklaus. Not just because he's a great golfer, but also because he's maintained such a high standard over such a long period. You get a lot of good golfers who may win a couple of tournaments. But Jack goes on year after year.

Another top star in my book if Bjorn Borg. Perhaps I admire him for the same reason as I like Jack Nicklaus. He's a brilliant player and he's consistent as well. I think his record at Wimbledon speaks for itself. I've been to Wimbledon a couple of times and it's a great occasion. It's like having Cup

Final day lasting for a fortnight!

Two other sports I like to watch are rugby and cricket. But those are two games that I think you have to know a lot about the technicalities before you can really enjoy them and understand what's happening. Still, that doesn't stop me going to Twickenham to cheer on Ireland when I get the chance.

You can see when it comes to other sports I'm more a spectator than a performer. But like most footballers I like to watch and appreciate the skill of other sportsmen. When it comes to hard work, application and concentration they're not all that different from footballers!

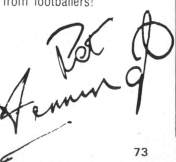

BJORN BORG — consistent champion

A BLAST FROM

Study the pictures below. The action's exciting, the faces are strangely familiar but . . . WHO ARE THEY?

To help you out, we will say that each one is a famous football personality as he was some years ago. Perhaps your dad will be able to help you — but if he gets confused too, you'll find the answers on Page 123.

2. No. 5 signed Jimmy Greaves for West Ham.

1. Barcelona once tried to get this man to become their manager.

3. The striker in white gave great service to Leeds United.

4. Beardless inside-forward.

5. He's managed many clubs!

74

THE PAST!

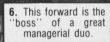

8. He's a manager now and he scored against West Germany in Mexico, 1970, for England.

6. This forward is the "boss" of a great managerial duo.

7. A Liverpool team group taken in 1951, but can you spot the famous face?

9. He ranks among the all-time greats in football management.

10. At one time he held the cap record for Northern Ireland.

11. This chap in the foreground learnt a lot from Joe Mercer.

OSVALDO ARDILES

'' My job is to destroy defences and create openings for others.''

MASCOT MAD!

In a time when football attendances are dwindling, any idea to bring the fans back is welcomed. From the North American Soccer League came a crowd-pleasing novelty which certainly went down well with the public — the MASCOT!

British soccer clubs are now jumping on the mascot-mad bandwagon, and no doubt we'll soon see some strange supporters in grounds up and down the country — just like these ...

Having a rest here is the bear mascot of the Washington Diplomats. Wonder if any of our clubs would have Hercules, Britain's best-loved runaway bear, for a mascot?

Not to be outdone by the Yanks, here's Chelsea's official mascot, a lovely lion called Stamford. No doubt his job's to ''roar'' on the Blues!

Here's Bugs Bunny, the official mascot of American soccer club Cosmos. Wonder what he says when they score? ''Nnnnaaaa — what's up, Doc?'' Or would it be, ''Gee, what an eighteen carrot goal!''

As well as animal mascots, many Stateside clubs employ official crowd pleasers to keep the fans happy. Mind you, if my team was four goals down it would take more than these two characters to put a smile on my face!

THIS GOALIE'S GOT GUTS

GOAL! WHAT A SCORCHER FROM FRANKIE MORGAN!

Thanks mainly to the brilliance of their young goalkeeper Ben Leiper, Mancastor City have won through to the F.A. Cup Final where they are due to play First Division pace-setters Swinton Rovers. But in a League match against Swinton only a matter of weeks before the Final, Ben's confidence in goal is taking a severe denting from Swinton's English international striker Frankie Morgan . . .

Blimey! Leiper looked half asleep there! A class 'keeper would've got to it — even though it was bending!

You wouldn't know a "class" 'keeper from a hole in the ground, mate! Ben Leiper's the best goalie in England!

Then, in the next attack . . .

Sure enough . . .

GOAL! ANOTHER ONE FOR SWINTON!

Look — Leiper's fumbled it again! And right at Frankie Morgan's feet — he must score!

Thanks, Foghorn, but he's right! Morgan caught me out there!

Then, in the closing seconds . . .

Morgan's through again! And look at Leiper! He doesn't know whether it's breakfast time or a week next Tuesday!

OUT, BEN! NARROW THE ANGLE!

But . . . . . IT'S IN! That's Frankie Morgan's hat-trick!

RUBBISH, CITY! AND DON'T BOTHER TURNING UP AT WEMBLEY, LEIPER! MORGAN WILL GET A DOZEN!

Sorry, lads! I let you down there! I was terrible!

Forget it, Ben! Just hope we can get things together before we play 'em in the F.A. Cup Final in a couple of weeks!

But in the last League match a week before Wembley . . .

COR! Leiper's still got the jitters! We don't stand a chance against Swinton next week!

Phew! He got it at the second attempt! Lucky it wasn't Frankie Morgan up against him there!

GOOD RECOVERY, BEN!

Full-time . . .

Better stay at home next week, Leiper! Morgan will run rings round you!

Ignore them, Ben! You'll be back to your usual self next week!

But that night . . .

NO . . . NO DON'T SHOOT!

Worried sick, Ben goes to see "Baldy" Brissen, the City manager . . .

DROP YOU? Are you out of your mind, Ben? I know you're going through a sticky patch, but it'll pass . . .

79

RAY CLEMENCE

"You have to be thick-skinned to be a goalkeeper."

The last time we played Swinton Frankie Morgan put three past me! I'm frightened I'll let the boys down again!

Okay, Ben, I can see that it's no good arguing with you! But I'll name you as sub in case you change your mind . . .

And when the team is announced . . .

JEEPERS! You've been dropped, Ben!

At my own request, Frank! But don't worry — Jackie won't let us down!

I don't know what to say, Ben! A Wembley Cup Final appearance . . . phew!

Saturday . . .

ROVERS! ROVERS!

CITY FOR THE CUP!

Thanks to reserve 'keeper Jackie Trent, City survive early Swinton pressure . . .

GREAT SAVE, JACKIE!

Time after time Jackie thwarts Swinton's ace striker Frankie Morgan . . .

But then, with twenty minutes gone . . .

CRIKEY! SORRY, KID!

AAAHH!

The City trainer is called on . . .

Sam's bringing him off — must be pretty bad! Okay, Ben! Get stripped — !

Well, that's the Cup lost! Everyone knows Leiper can't handle Frankie Morgan!

Don't you believe it, chum! There's NOBODY Ben Leiper can't handle!

82

83

IT'S THERE! WHAT A MOVE! AND BEN LEIPER STARTED IT ALL!

Ben is back to his brilliant best . . .

Then, with the scores still level and just minutes to go . . .

Well taken, Ben, but watch out for Morgan!

Looks like he's coming for me! Maybe it's about time I showed him who's boss of this penalty area!

YEE — AAARGHH!

See!? I can handle you any time, Morgan! **JUST REMEMBER THAT!**

And from Ben's clearance . . .

I've left my marker, but the 'keeper's coming out! It'll be touch and go . . .

MADE IT! THAT'S GOT TO BE THE WINNER!

Full-time!

Well played, Ben! I thought I had you there, but I guess you won through in the end! You're still the best there is!

And you're the best number 9 in the business, Frankie! Well played, mate!

You did it, Ben! You sorted yourself out —!

And just in time, eh, boss? **C'MON! RECKON WE'VE GOT A BIT OF SIVERWARE TO COLLECT!**

THE END

SPORTS CROSS=WORD

TEST YOUR SPORTING KNOWLEDGE

He used to play for Brighton. (see 15 down)

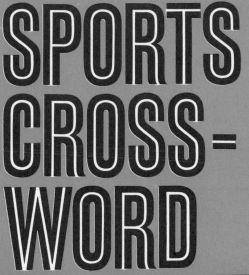

He was a world champion in 1980. (see 2 down)

ACROSS

7. THIS SCOTTISH TEAM PLAYS AT RECREATION PARK (5)
8. No. 7 USED TO BE CALLED AN __ RIGHT (7)
9. LIVERPOOL'S GROUND (7)
10. COUNTY SIDE IN ENGLAND (5)
12. SOMEONE WHO PLAYS FOR TOTTENHAM? (4)
14. THE __ NELSON GOLF CLASSIC (5)
17. A ROYAL RACE COURSE (5)
18. WEST BROM'S OWEN (4)
21. A TOP IRISH GOLFER (5)
23. THEY'VE LIVED IN LIVERPOOL'S SHADOW FOR YEARS (7)
25. FORMER MOTHER-WELL, LEICESTER AND RANGERS PLAYER (7)
26. NICKNAMED THE " POTTERS " (5)

DOWN

1. THE REAL NAME OF A SHINTY STICK (5)
2. __ THORBURN (5)
3. A LIVERPOOL PLAYER (4)
4. VANBURN __ WORCESTER BOWLER (6)
5. THE LEGENDARY MATTHEWS (4)
6. FOR THIS, YOUR FOOTBALL TEAM IS AWARDED TWO POINTS (7)
11. A BUNKER FOR BRITAIN, A __ TRAP IN THE U.S.A. (4)
13. 2 DOWN TRYS TO DO THIS OFTEN (3)
14. BRIAN HOOPER TRIES TO CLEAR THIS (3)
15. TOP FOREST STRIKER (4)
16. ABERDEEN'S COLOUR (7)
18. MECHANICS USE THIS ON REAR AXLES OF MOTOR-RACING CARS (6)
19. FOUND IN A BOXER'S CORNER (5)
20. HALF OF MILAN (5)
22. ST. MARTIN, THE FRENCH JOCKEY (4)
24. WHEN YOUR TEAM'S 5-0 UP, YOU CHANT THIS (4)

Astonishingly enough, Pat was the only serious casualty, but just how serious wasn't known then . . .

Only one bad casualty — it's Pat Mahoney!

Oh, no! Hope he'll be okay.

Pat's heart had stopped beating twice while he lay injured on the track and only expert medical attention had saved him. He "died" a third time on his way to hospital, where he was immediately rushed to intensive care . . .

It's bad! Seconds count!

Only Pat's incredible fitness pulled him through the nightmare alive, but he was desperately ill . . .

He's passed the worst, Dad, but the doctors aren't sure if he'll ever recover completely.

They told me he'd be in a wheelchair when he leaves here . . . It's very — very sad, Darryl, and you his fiancee too!

Pat was in a wheelchair when he left the hospital three months later but already his incredible will-to-win was urging him on . . .

Six months to come in a Rehabilitation Centre. I'm not going to be in a wheelchair when I leave there!

And so . . .

You're walking, Pat! I can hardly believe it!

It's . . . only the . . . beginning, Darryl!

Got to keep the exercise going . . .

Sure enough in the weeks and months that followed . . .

But the fight for physical fitness wasn't Pat's only battle. He had to teach himself to read, write, speak and even eat properly again!

Got to keep working . . . trying . . .

That's better! Things are going well!

87

The thumbs-up sign from Jim Clark as he crosses the finishing line of the 1965 Indy 500.

GEARED FOR VICTORY

The Indianapolis 500 had an unenviable reputation. The two-and-a-half-mile oval circuit, only 55 feet wide and with banked corners, was the fastest and most dangerous car race in the world. Since its inception in 1911, it had claimed many lives while becoming a specialist event in which international Grand Prix drivers had never seriously challenged the American supremacy.

In 1965, however, a 29-year-old Scot changed all that. Jim Clark, double Formula One World Drivers' Champion, had previously contested this unique event, but that year, in a specially-built Lotus Mk 38. designed by Colin Chapman, Jim was geared up to win — and he did!

At an average speed of 150.686 m.p.h., he finished two laps ahead of second-placed Parnelli Jones and established himself as one of motor racing's all-time greats.

The look of a champion at the Indianapolis Speedway!

With Brian Jacks, Darius Goodwin and Pat Jennings all talking about their favourite sports and sportstars we thought it might be a good idea to look at the way some now famous sports began and who better to ask than . . .

KLOG

OUR STONE AGE SOCCER STAR

TAP!

IN THE BEGINNING, GOLFERS WORRIED ABOUT GETTING 'BIRDIES'. . .

. . . BUT MORE OFTEN ABOUT BIRDIES GETTING *THEM!*

THE ORIGINS OF JAVELIN THROWING
ARE OBVIOUS ENOUGH...

...HOWEVER, FEW PEOPLE REALISE THAT **SQUASH**
STARTED AT THE SAME TIME *!*

AND FINALLY, CRICKET.
WHY THE BIG BAT,
YOU ASK ?

YOU SHOULD HAVE SEEN
THE SIZE OF THE WICKETS *!*

Super Sharron

WE DON'T produce too many top class swimmers in Britain, do we? What names can you come up with? Super-Scot David Wilkie from a few years back maybe. The distinctive Duncan Goodhew, probably. And then, of course, there's Sharron Davies . . .

Sharron hit the headlines in the 1978 Commonwealth Games with two firsts, one second and one third. Then two years later came one fourth and a silver medal at the Moscow Olympics.

"It's amazing how the whole thing grew," recalled Sharron. "I didn't take up swimming until I was six, as a general hobby. It soon got into my blood though and in 1970 I began to get involved in training and competition.

"I suppose you could say I took like a duck to water, but any success I've ever had has been down — not only to me — but to all the help I've had over the years from my family.

"Not only did they make a lot of sacrifices to give me every chance of making it in swimming, but my father coached me as well! He was a hard taskmaster, kept pushing me to work harder. But that's the attitude anybody needs to succeed."

Sharron's right, of course. Determination is a must for any sportstar. But just as important is enjoyment. For Sharron THE great attraction of swimming is that she just enjoys being in the water.

"Yes, swimming's great fun," Sharron added. "Though I'll have a go at most sports really. My favourites are horse-riding, surfing/sailing, canoeing, badminton, squash and rugby. Yes, rugby!

"I wouldn't say that any of them help me directly with my swimming, but they all help to keep me fit, and agile. I always think that if you stay fit and healthy, you stay happy. I enjoy fitness training.

"Besides swimming, I do weights, circuits, running, flexibility and resistance work and use the swim bench. That keeps me busy!"

Fitness and enjoyment apart though, there's one other quality that anybody needs to succeed in sport — the obvious one, talent. So we asked Sharron who she tipped to make it to the top in swimming.

"I think you should look out for Suki Brownsdon and Andy Jameson," Sharron replied. "They're both naturally good technically. On top of that, they're determined, versatile and intelligent. Also they want to win and they're happy in what they're doing. Given the breaks, they could go far."

So a bright future is forecast for Suki and Andy, but one of the problems budding swimming stars like these two inevitably face is the challenge from the "Eastern Bloc" countries like Russia and East Germany . . .

"I really respect the East Germans," Sharron told Scoop. "Maybe they do get a lot of help, but they do train under very hard conditions and they're forced to work long hours.

"When it comes to competition they do their jobs well and they're friendly when they're allowed to be. To be honest I don't think we can compete on equal terms with the Eastern European countries at the moment, we need more facilities and finance at the grass roots.

"Given that, the U.K. could do well, because there is talent around. Speaking personally, swimming's been good to me. So go on, have a go yourself. Take a trip down to your local pool and have a dip.

"After all, the more youngsters who take up swimming, the more chance we have of taking on and beating the rest of the world!!"

94

95

ROSCOE TANNER

'' My service is the strong part of my game—and it's been timed at 140 m.p.h..''

G

Paul's good! I could let him beat me quick and nip away to me tennis final . . .

. . . but that wouldn't be fair to the audience! I gotta put up a good fight!

Cor! Nice shot, Paul! Forced me to play into the net! First game to you!

Buster hits back in the second set . . .

Second game to Buster 21-19. They'll have to go to three for the decider! This is terrific stuff!

Minutes later . . .

Buster, they're getting near to matchpoint in the mixed doubles on telly!

BLIMEY! And we're halfway through this last game! Thanks, chum! What we need here is a quick decision!

HERE WE GO! WIN OR BUST!

Buster hits dynamic form . . .

That's it! You've beaten me, Buster! Crikey, you were really powering it over those last few points!

Great game, Paul! Gotta go! Say thanks to the organisers for me!

Buster's coach, Clive Neville, is waiting outside . . .

You're here at last! Anybody else would have cried off the ping-pong! All right, Buster, get in! Your tennis gear is in the back!

Thanks, Clive! Step on it, mate! I'll change on the way!

At the court . . .

HEY! Players only through this entrance!

Well, I ain't dressed like this to go to a fancy-dress party, mate! Anyroad, I can't stop! I'm due on court any second now!

98

99

BE BRAVE!

FOOTBALL is a tough physical game and hard knocks are part of it. Every player knows this and accepts it — but there are lots of situations where a bit of bravery is called for.

It's a must for the goalie who's to go down for a ball in a mass of players with boots flying. And a goalie has to be brave to go down on the ball at the feet of a forward all set to shoot at goal. In both cases the 'keeper has to take a risk — he knows perfectly well the danger involved. But despite this he goes in looking for the ball. That's being really brave.

Defenders, too, must show quite a bit of courage. Going up for a high ball in a crowded goalmouth or making a desperate last gasp tackle can all bring a big chance of injury or a nasty knock. Even standing in a defensive wall with some dead-ball expert about to take a free-kick can call for a lot of courage. When you see a free-kick taken and it smashes off the wall, remember it may well have rebounded off some player's nose! But it's not just goalkeepers' and defenders who need to show a bit of bravery. Every player who goes for a fifty-fifty ball, or makes a tackle, knows he's taking a risk. Nine times out of ten there'll be no problem — but every so often a player will be left slumped on the ground.

And sometimes that's where the real bravery has to be shown. Injuries can often mean a long worrying time out of action — with the added problem of wondering just how long before the injury recovers — or even if it will ever be cured. Players worry, too, about whether they'll get their place back in the team once they are fit. Perhaps the player who stepped into their position is playing so well he can't be left out.

An even bigger worry with a serious injury is whether or not it will end the victim's playing career altogether. Every season there are players who have to give up the game because of injury. Every player knows it could happen to them, but they have to put that kind of thought out of their mind before they get out there on the pitch.

It's pretty clear that footballers, like most sportsmen, have to be pretty brave when they're out there on the pitch. But often, too, a lot of courage has to be shown by players even when they're not playing. By that I mean players who're fighting back to full fitness after injury.

While the rest of the team are busy preparing for the next game the injured player will be on his own. Perhaps trudging up and down the terracing to strengthen damaged ankles. Or going through a lonely grind in the gym, building up muscles weakened by lack of action.

To train and work so hard knowing that, no matter how much effort you put in, there'll be no game for you that week is a heart-breaking experience. Yet some players have gone through this routine for week after week, sometimes for months.

One player from last season who readily comes to mind is Trevor Francis, Britain's first million pound player. He had to sit on the sidelines for match after match. Stricken by an Achilles tendon injury, he could only watch as his team won the European Cup in 1980. Then he was still on the sidelines when Forest made a faltering start to the season's league campaign — and then were put out of the European Cup in the early stages.

Eventually, after a long, hard slog, Trevor made it back into the Forest first team. You need to be brave to face up to setbacks like that

But players know that's the sort of situation they have to be prepared to face up to. It's all part of a footballer's life!

Kenny Dalglish

You need to be brave to make saves like this. Pat Jennings is the keeper in the firing line.

TREVOR FRANCIS, NOTTINGHAM FOREST

101

Inter Milan keeper Sarti can only grasp at air as Tommy Gemmell, all but hidden on the left of the picture, blasts Celtic's equaliser.

CELTIC – PRIDE OF EUROPE

During the mid-1960s European football was in the grip of the defence-minded Italians. By scoring few goals, but conceding even fewer, A.C. Milan and their fierce rivals Inter Milan had won three European Cups between them — but made few friends in the process.

So in 1967 when Celtic, managed by Jock Stein and having won everything open to them that season, became the first British club to reach the final, not just Scotland but all of Europe was hoping for a performance and result that would put paid to the static Italian style of play.

The game didn't start well for Celtic, however, when they conceded an early penalty goal — but after that Inter never knew what hit them. With Johnstone and Lennox buzzing on the wings, Wallace, Chalmers and Auld pressuring the defence, and McNeill marshalling his defence to blot out the Milan attack, Celtic then released their secret weapon — Tommy Gemmell.

The attacking full-back with the rocket shot moved up as the Italian defence was pulled one way then the other, and when the ball landed at his feet outside the penalty area he cannoned the ball into the net for the equaliser.

Only keeper Sarti kept Milan in the game after that with some inspired play but five minutes from time he had to admit defeat for a second time. As a Willie Wallace shot powered its way towards the Milan goal, Steve Chalmers deflected it into the net for the winning goal.

Pure football had defeated cynical style — and all Europe celebrated.

Sarti is stranded once again as Steve Chalmers deflects the ball into the net for the winning goal...

. . . and Billy McNeill becomes the first British captain to lift the massive European Cup.

SPEEDWAY–
THE FAMILY SPORT

I t's said, and not without good reason, that speedway's a friendly sport, a sport for all the family. Look around the terraces and you'll find fans from five to ninety-five, from toddlers to grans, mixing freely with rival supporters.

And the family connection doesn't end on the terraces. Speedway's a sport which abounds in fathers and sons, brothers—and even, in at least one case, brother and sister—on the riding side of the safety fence.

There's now quite a tradition of sons following in father's footsteps—or should it be tyretracks? Ace tuner Guy Allott follows the fortunes of son Nicky at the tracks at which he used to star. Neil Middleditch's dad Ken was one of England's top riders in the fifties. Nig Close's father Derek was a favourite at the same time.

Jim Lightfoot, Clive Featherby, Vic White and Harry Bastable can now watch sons Rob, Craig, Keith and Steve, respectively battle for points in re-runs of their epic duels of the '60's.

CONTINUED OVER

Happy family! Ivan Mauger with son Kym, mother and wife Raye.

The most successful of the Kennett clan, Gordon.

Oh, brother! Glasgow's Charlie and Kenny McKinna.

A sight you won't see in British league racing—Elizabeth, sister of former world champion Anders, in full flight.

If you notice a similarity in style that's not surprising. Tony Briggs rides the inside line while father Barry takes the outside.

Billy Bales and spectacular Kiwi Graham Warren thrilled the crowds over twenty years ago and currently Ray and Mark are chips off the old block.

It's two other famous Kiwis who have created the most interest in the past couple of seasons, however. The on-track meetings of Briggs and Mauger attracted huge crowds in the sixties and seventies as Barry and Ivan captured ten world titles between them. Now it's the turn of the second generation, with Tony Briggs and Kym Mauger set to continue the family rivalry into the eighties—and perhaps the nineties! And of course, Ivan's had the opportunity of actually lining up against young Kym, an experience which he admits he found quite disturbing!

Not that members of the same family racing against each other is by any means uncommon. In the 1938 World Final, for example, Cordy Milne secured third place—while brother Jack took the title. A decade later, England's top star Jack Parker, reckoned to be the best rider never to be World Champion, had a worthy rival in kid brother Norman.

In recent years, Tom and Joe Owen, Gordon, Dave and Barney Kennett, Jimmy and Bobby Beaton (whose father, Jimmy senior, promotes at Glasgow where Charlie and Kenny McKinna are also to be found), Scottish farmers Doug and Willie Templeton who gave almost a combined half century's service to the sport, Mick and Andy Hines, Czechs Jan and Vaclav Verner, American aces Kelly and Shawn Moran, Chris and Dave Morton, Alan, Andy and John Grahame and Superswedes Jan and Bjorn Andersson are among the many who have temporarily set aside "brotherly-love" to race each other.

Of course, the most celebrated brothers are those of the Collins clan, tracking almost an entire team themselves! Indeed Peter, Les, Phil and Neil competed as a family on several occasions in Four-team tournaments—and youngest brother Steven is still waiting in the wings (or should that be pits?)

Going one better, perhaps, is former world Champion Anders Michanek, whose sister rides regularly in their native Sweden! It's a situation which couldn't happen in this country, but Elizabeth has shown herself to be the equal of her male opponents many a time.

Speedway's history really is full of family connections. The distinctive and special speedway smell of burning methanol certainly seems to be addictive once it gets in the blood. The question now is which family is going to claim the first grandfather, father and son in the sport . . . ?!

Families at war! Tom Owen, brother of Joe, and Neil Middleditch, son of Ken, dice for the lead.

THE COLLINS BROTHERS

Peter is hoisted on the shoulders of Phil and Les, with Steven and Neil kneeling.

"**S**NAPPER" SCOTT, Ironfield Rovers' centrehalf, checked his run and turned back up the field, his body sagging slightly in resignation. He knew there was no chance of getting the less-than-fiftyfifty ball.

The Merton United centrehalf was already halfway there, and out of the corner of his eye Snapper had caught sight of a hostile striker streaking for an open space. He noticed, too, that one of his team-mates had picked up the Merton centre.

"You lazy so-and-so, Scott! Why don't you chase the ball?" The disgusted cry of an Ironfield Rovers' fan reached his ears.

"Maybe it would've meant he'd have to tackle," another Rovers' fan taunted, drawing an assenting grumble from a section of the crowd.

Snapper glared up into the sea of faces. He knew what they said — that he wasn't a grafter, that he flinched from the rough stuff . . . that he only shone when it suited him and faded when the chips were down.

He moved beside the striker, shutting out any chance of a pass. The Merton centre-half looked around desperately for a way of penetrating the Rovers' defence — now sealed solidly by Snapper's move — and in desperation hit the ball into the penalty area in the hope of a lucky break. Snapper had the satisfaction of watching a team-mate turn the ball back safely to the 'keeper.

Later, a fierce battle developed in front of the Merton goal. Snapper stayed on the edge of the penalty area knowing that a lucky break would give him a chance of scoring. He saw Bertie West, the Ironfield centre, get his foot to the ball.

"Back . . . back with it," Snapper screamed.

Bertie released the ball and Snapper moved. His thigh muscles rippled as he hit the ball with his left foot, curving it past the scramble of players and the unsighted 'keeper into the back of the net. The crowd roared their approval but Snapper's only reaction was to clear his throat and spit before turning back upfield.

The sharp nose and aggressive thrust of his head gave him the prowling, restless appearance of a predatory animal. The face was lean, tanned to mahogany by wind and sun and when his lips parted into a snarl it was to reveal chipped and broken teeth — the victims of many an aerial battle for the ball. Not a vestige of fat showed on the squat frame that was obviously tuned to super-fitness.

A minute or two later the final whistle shrilled. It was a two-one victory for Rovers.

The crowd roared as the Rovers trotted back to the tunnel with Snapper at the rear. He heard someone call: "Good old Snapper" and waved his hand in the direction. But he hadn't forgotten what they'd said when he failed to chase that fiftyfifty ball.

He knew how fickle fans were and how little they understood sometimes. They didn't seem to realise, for example, that he always turned it on when he had to — that he was of much more use to the team keeping out of trouble and avoiding injury.

"Same again for the Cuptie?" Mel Fenton, the Rovers' manager grinned at them as they made their way to the dressing room.

"Wouldn't mind," said Snapper. "But that's a different proposition."

"The understatment of the year," laughed Bertie West.

"Skegworth are good . . . hardly lost a game at home this season. Pity we're away to them," added one of the backs.

"Not to worry," said Snapper . . . then noticing a young apprentice hovering at the dressing room door: "Oi, you . . . take these boots and make a better job of cleaning 'em than you did last time!"

FLU EPIDEMIC!

BOTH Skegworth Town and the Rovers were Second Division teams. The two towns lay fifteen miles from each other and their Fifth Round F.A. Cup tie, scheduled for the following Saturday, had the extra significance of being a local derby.

On Sunday, Snapper scanned the sports pages. Several reporters praised his goal but one labelled him a glory hunter and gave Bertie West the credit for getting the ball out of the scramble in the first place.

Snapper muttered his disgust. What did reporters know? What could Bertie have done with the ball? Nothing . . . but he, Snapper, had seen how the situation could develop. Why didn't the dim-witted reporter give him credit for that?

The first signs of a flu epidemic began to show themselves on Monday. Two reserves hadn't turned up for training and Bertie West was coughing and finding everything an effort. By Wednesday the toll included Bertie and two members of the first team. On Thursday the situation was desperate. Five of the club's top players and several reserves were on the sick list.

Snapper watched the reserve centre "Shanks" Tonnington — a lanky nineteen-year-old with great potential — being put through his paces in a kickabout.

"Move . . . get in! Get the ball . . . first time!" Snapper directed harshly. Later, he'd ease up and offer some advice if he felt the lad was worthy of it.

"Assert yourself . . . get in! Never mind the fairyfeet stuff," he continued, as Shanks struggled through the kick-about.

The lad let fly, cracking the ball high over the goals.

He turned to Snapper in exasperation.

"You're one to talk. You don't do a lot of running about yourself, do you? I don't see you in the centre of much rough stuff!"

Snapper's mouth fell open — making him look for a moment like a mahogany version of Kermit the Frog. Then it snapped shut again as he advanced on the young player.

"I do what's needed, son. When your team-mates can depend on you the way they can on me, then you're halfway to being a professional."

"That's your opinion." The lad turned away blushing, still indignant. It didn't do for reserves to argue with established first-team members but Snapper's constant shouting had got him on the raw. Besides, Shanks knew in his bones that he, himself, would be good one day . . . a lot better than Snapper Scott.

Snapper snorted. He'd have to keep an eye on that one. He had all the makings of a budding prima-donna. And sometimes that type didn't have a lot of guts.

THE CUP-TIE

ON Saturday nobody gave much for Ironfield's chances and when the teams took the field the Skegworth fans sang and waved their banners as if victory was already theirs. The Ironfield supporters took up the challenge and launched spiritedly into their song, but to Snapper's ears, long attuned to songs and chants on cup-tie days, the Ironfield voices had a hollow ring. They made him think of a large animal growling at bay — and its fury could quickly turn on friend and foe alike.

He glanced at Shanks Tonnington as the young striker practised some shots at goal. The youngster's face was white and tense and Snapper knew that he would soon know what the lad was made of.

Skegworth won the toss and, using the left wing, moved quickly upfield. Snapper covered the Skegworth centre as an Ironfield back moved out to meet the challenge from the wing, but the winger dribbled past and sent a high cross into the penalty area. Snapper and

PROFESSIONAL

the centre raced for it. Snapper's head got there first — he nodded hard across the line for a corner.

Snapper headed the ball clear from the corner . . . but almost at once it was back, lost by one of his own forwards and punted into the Ironfield area by the Skegworth centre-half. This time the inexperience of the young Ironfield reserves was glaringly evident. Two of them hesitated over a dropping ball and a Skegworth striker nipped between them and drove a shot at goal. The Ironfield 'keeper had no chance. It was one-nil.

"Clowns! Call yourselves football players?" Snapper shouted furiously.

The second Skegworth attack ten minutes later tore the Ironfield defence apart. A chip shot caught the 'keeper off his line and the score was two-nil.

As the attacks continued, gaining in confidence and ferocity, Snapper bawled and shouted . . . groaned, encouraged, raged, but everything fell on deaf ears. Another goal was narrowly prevented by a masterly save.

In all, Ironfield made four sallies up field. On one of them Shanks Tonnington got the ball.

"Draw your man . . . then pass!" Snapper shouted at him.

Shanks drew his man, beat him and ploughed on.

"Cripes! I'm clear," thought Snapper . . . he should pass. But nerves had seized the lad. He raced on, oblivious of all but the Skegworth goal. He ran straight into a defender and lost the ball. Groans came from the Ironfield fans.

Skegworth piled on the pressure as half-time approached, bombarding the Ironfield goal from all angles. Snapper could hardly believe their luck when the whistle blew and they were only two-nil down.

As they left the field the Ironfield fans' moans and groans became open abuse.

"Take up knitting, Scott!" one of them bayed.

"Yeah, there's a place for you in an old folks' home," another bawled.

"The whole team should be in there."

Snapper hung his head. But he knew things would have been a lot worse if it hadn't been for him.

He listened as the manager launched into his gee-up spiel — exhorting and encouraging and advising on tactics. But he knew the advice was lost. The young reserves would try their hardest, but they just didn't have the experience to cope. There was a haunted, wounded flicker in their eyes. It was unfortunate that they should have been thrown in at the deep end like this.

He knew now that their Cup hopes hinged on his experience. Now was the time to use every ounce of skill.

Continued on page 123

107

BORG

THE DATE — NOVEMBER 1980: THE TIME — 9.30 a.m.: THE PLACE — STOCKHOLM, SWEDEN . . . and the great Bjorn Borg astounds attendant Pressmen by admitting that he had enjoyed a "late night celebration" the previous evening. Up till then, Borg was regarded as perhaps the most dedicated tennis pro in the business, certainly one of the fittest, and undoubtedly one who was determined to hold on to his No. 1 world ranking. So, was his super-fit, super-dedicated image slipping . . . ?

No chance! It was just that the day before had brought him the Swedish Open title for the first time in seven years of trying — and quite rightly so, the blond Swede decided to let his hair down!

And those who had previously labelled him "Ice-Borg" because of his apparent lack of feeling as he stayed cool in the most tense on-court moments, were stunned and surprised as he proved that he was actually HUMAN!

Bjorn Rune Borg has long given the impression on tennis courts that he isn't quite human. Unbeaten in more than half a decade at Wimbledon, he has developed a unique combination of skill, athleticism and incredible concentration which often causes opponents to wilt before Borg puts ball to racquet.

For all his wonderful record — and it would take more than these two pages to detail it — Borg *has* remained remarkably human. He's not the unfeeling robot of tennis that he's reputed to be, but a warm individual who still phones home to his parents to find out how the local ice-hockey team at Sodertalje got on. And just try getting him and his soccer-daft Swedish mates away from the television when there's a big game being played!

Nobody can deny that his brilliance on court has brought him a life of luxury: fast cars, a house amongst Monaco's millionaires, he even jumps on aeroplanes from anywhere in the world to visit his dentist in Stockholm! But don't let anyone tell you that success has made him immune from the enjoyment or despair of his tennis — it hasn't! That was proved beyond doubt on a cold November morning in 1980.

Too often the title "Superstar" is used to describe today's sportsmen, but if one man above all others deserves it, then surely that man is the King of the Courts — Bjorn Borg!

THE COX KID

Kenny Cox plays for First Division Ranford City, who are at home for the first leg of the World Club Championship match against the Condors, a team from the South American country of Castilla . . .

KEEP GOING, KENNY! TAKE THEM ON!

MISSED ME, PAL!

The centre half's coming to me and leaving Vincent Dalgety in the clear!

Yours, Dalgety!

GOAL!

Dalgety, the City striker, is a favourite with the fans —

Dalgety collects the cheers, but you made that goal, Kenny.

It don't matter who scores 'em! They all count!

Later —

They're after the equaliser. Their striker's coming in for the cross. I'll get to him.

Yours, Freddy!

Well covered, Kenny!

Good kick, Freddy. That should put Dalgety clean through.

COR! HE'S MISSED A REAL SITTER!

Minutes later, City are on the attack again . . .

FOUL, REF!

That glory hunter's lost the ball!

The ref ain't giving out awards for acting, Dalgety! Up on your feet and back in the game quick, you big ham!

Let's have it back, chum!

MICKY THOMAS

" I'm fiercely Welsh and proud of it. I like to have the words ' Manchester United and Wales ' after my name."

Let's see if I can get this second goal.

TO ME, COX!

So you can lose it again or miss it? You must be joking!

A banana bender, mate.

URR!

I didn't expect the kid to shoot! I thought he would beat Manuel first!

Full-time . . .

Two-nil! It'll have to do. But we'd be going into the second-leg with a bigger lead if you'd given me better service, Cox.

Yeah? If you believe that, you'll believe anything, Dalgety.

Dorando, the Condors' manager, discusses the game with his coach . . .

We shall have to do better in Castilla, or our jobs are in danger, Senor Dorando. But how do we stop Cox?

That young roughneck isn't going to lose me my job! If we can't stop him on the field, we'll stop him some other way!

A week later, City are in Castilla for the return leg . . .

Condors are a good team, and we look forward to a close game. But I'm hoping to be among the goals again.

Dalgety's enjoying the limelight but I hate all this hanging about before matches. I'm going to my room.

Thanks, chum, but I reckon I can manage that myself. I ain't the type for the Jeeves bit.

Si, senor!

Hey, what are you doing in my case, mate?

I am the room-servant, senor. I was tidying your clothes!

BALL BOY

SCOOP QUIZ

1. Ipswich had a great U.E.F.A. Cup run last season. Here an Ipswich player wins a heading duel against Bohemians Prague. Who is he?

2. What is Ipswich Town's home ground called?

3. Who scored Ipswich's winning goal in the 1978 F.A. Cup Final?

4. Floodlit cricket came to Britain in 1980 with a match between Essex and the West Indies. Which soccer ground was the venue?

5. Did Graham Dilley play for England in any of their Test matches against the West Indies in the Caribbean last winter?

6. For which county does Wayne Larkins play?

7. Must a jockey carry a whip?

8. Which horse won the 1980 Epsom Derby — was it Henbit, Troy or Ela-Mana-Mou?

9. On which course is the Grand National held?

10. If the anchor girl in a 4 x 400 metres relay race is injured shortly before the race begins, can one of her three remaining team-mates run two stages of the race?

11. Name the athlete below.

12. How many athletics gold medals did Britain win at the Moscow Olympics?

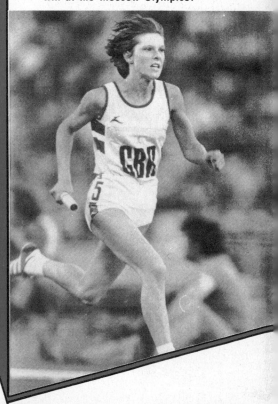

13. A British boxer lands a spectacular left hook while retaining his world title — who is he?

14. Unjumble these letters to find the name of a British world champion from the 1970s. HNOJ YTRESAC.

15. What does B.B.B.C. stand for?

16. This gent below seems to have landed himself the job of *pulling* two golfing trollies, but perhaps he's better known for playing in a soccer team which has *pushed* for the First Division title during much of 1981. Who is he?

17. A former Villa player scored the only goal of the 1980 League Cup Final while playing for another Midlands club. Who was he?

18. Name the Midlands club which plays at Meadow Lane.

19. Bjorn Borg takes an early "break" in a match. In which year did he first win the Wimbledon singles title?

20. Are their any restrictions on the size of a tennis racket?

21. What is the name of the trophy competed for every year by British professional women players and their American opposite numbers?

(Answers on page 123)

PICTURE POWER

It happens in a fraction of a second and is lost for ever. Or at least it would be if it wasn't captured on film. Today's sophisticated camera equipment can freeze time — or in some cases extend it — so that the drama which was played out before your very eyes, and then vanished, can be recorded and preserved.

With the use of special lenses and the tricks of their trade, photographers can take you into the heart of the action and even "create" situations which the eye can't see. Get the picture . . .?

Speedway races can be won or lost at the starting gate — and Mike Ferreira's little more than a blur as he jets away from the outside grid.

It takes real skill to freeze the action at just the right time, as it is in this award-winning picture of Kevin Keegan being sent flying by Belgian defender Raymond Mommens.

Ballet — or a balancing act? It certainly doesn't seem to be cricket as Australian wicket-keeper Rodney Marsh strikes a pose more often seen at Covent Garden, while he delicately "places" the ball on the stumps in an attempt to run out Graham Gooch.

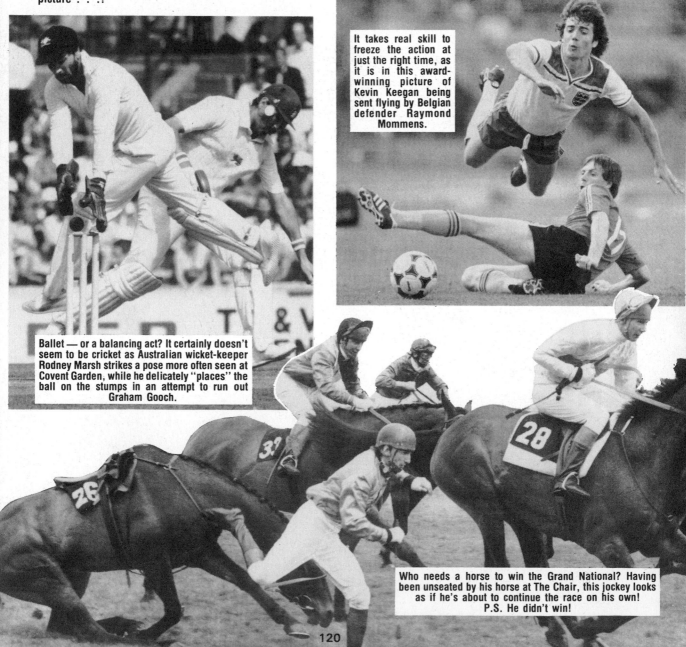

Who needs a horse to win the Grand National? Having been unseated by his horse at The Chair, this jockey looks as if he's about to continue the race on his own! P.S. He didn't win!

Just how many legs do rugby league players have!? If you look closely, however, you'll discover the "extra" legs belong to the Hull Kingston Rovers' player buried under his Warrington opponents!

Look — no car! Only the head and tail lights of this rally car remain as it competes in a night stage of the R.A.C. Rally.

With top speeds of 200 m.p.h. or above, sports cars can really turn on the power. This special zoom shot leaves you in no doubt that this car is travelling — fast!

Ouch! In the best traditions of Kung Fu, Arsenal's Frank Stapleton tries to make contact, while Liverpool defender Phil Neal obviously believes in the old adage of keeping his eye on the ball!

The camera can take you right into the middle of a scrum — and make you thankful it's not you involved in the action! Just look at the expressions on the faces in this encounter between Ireland and Scotland and imagine what each one might be thinking!

WAS IT THE GREATEST CLUB MATCH EVER?

If ever there was a battle of the gunslingers in football, the 1960 European Cup Final was it. Hampden Park, Glasgow, was packed with 127,621 fans to watch West German champions Eintracht Frankfurt, who had scored twelve goals against Rangers in the two-leg semi-final, take on Real Madrid, the Spanish aces who had won all four previous European Cups and whose name represented attacking football at its very best.

Although expectations were high, no-one could have forecast the feast of fast-flowing football the

game produced. The Germans were good, very good, but Real were simply magnificent. After allowing Eintracht the luxury of scoring the opening goal, the Real forward line of Canario, Del Sol, Di Stefano, Puskas and Gento ran riot. The final score-line of 7-3 for Real, with the teasing, tormenting Di Stefano scoring a hat-trick and the famous Puskas claiming four, only hints at the quality of the football served up by both teams.

This was Real at their very peak, however, and none of the crowd packed on to the Hampden slopes, or the millions who watched the game live on TV, would ever doubt that they had witnessed the greatest club match ever played.

The famous left foot of Ferenc Puskas hammers home Real's fourth goal from the penalty spot.

With all the skill and grace of a toreador, Alfredo D i Stefano slides Real's opening goal into the net.

ANSWERS TO JUMBO CROSSWORD—Pages 26-27

Across 10 — Stirrup. 11 — Halifax. 12 — Penhall. 15 — School. 16 — Archibald. 17 — Cannon. 18 — Spin. 20 — Eagle. 22 — Hales. 23 — Pate. 24 — Gritted. 25 — Isle. 26 — Glucose. 27 — Sore backs. 33 — Brighton. 34 — M. Riessen. 35 — Neale. 36 — Ray. 37 — Blackpool. 38 — Chi. 39 — Three goals. 41 — Odd. 42 — Age. 45 — Sweats. 46 — Fast dog. 47 — Becketts. 49 — Spot. 51 — Fired. 53 — Red. 54 — Olsen. 56 — Eric Bristow. 57 — Manchester Utd. coach.

Down 1 — Stockport. 2 — Trio. 3 — Bulls-eyes. 4 — Manchester City. 5 — Didi. 6 — Vava. 7 — Newcastle. 8 — Shin. 9 — Blood test. 13 — Badge. 14 — Idols. 19 — Nottingham. 21 — Whitbread Gold Cup. 22 — Hillclimb. 23 — Packed snow. 27 — Sin. 28 — Sam. 29 — Crenshaw. 30 — Street. 31 — Kicked. 32 — Red light. 40 — Leg break. 41 — Ole. 43 — Partick. 44 — Tension. 46 — Forest. 47 — Bad guy. 48 — Crowds. 50 — Park. 51 — Fore. 52 — Drop. 55 — Nice.

ANSWERS TO SPORTS CROSSWORD—Page 85

Across. 7 — Alloa. 8 — Outside. 9 — Anfield. 10 — Notts. 12 — Spur. 14 — Byron. 17 — Ascot. 18 — Gary. 21 — Darcy. 23 — Everton. 25 — Stevens. 26 — Stoke.

Down. 1 — Caman. 2 — Cliff. 3 — Case. 4 — Holder. 5 — Stan. 6 — Victory. 11 — Sand. 13 — Pot. 14 — Bar. 15 — Ward. 16 — Scarlet. 18 — Grease. 19 — Stool. 20 — Inter. 22 — Yves. 24 — Easy.

CORRECTED ANSWERS TO "TARGET TIME"—Page 39

1 — Greece. 2 — Belgium. 3 — Cosmos. 4 — Yugoslavia. 5 — Dundee United. 6 — No. 7 — St. Johnstone. 8 — Geoff Hurst. 9 — Paris. 10 — Werder Bremen. 11 — Home of Swansea City. 12 — False. 13 — Chester.

14 — Yes, a substitute can be played as long as the match hasn't started. 15 — Malta. 16 — They all played for West Ham. 17 — Tony Woodcock, while signed for Nottingham Forest. 18 — Bradford City.

ANSWERS TO "A BLAST FROM THE PAST"—Pages 74-75

1 — Bobby Robson. 2 — Ron Greenwood. 3 — Allan Clarke. 4 — Jimmy Hill. 5 — Tommy Docherty. 6 — Brian Clough. 7 — Bob Paisley. 8 — Alan Mullery. 9 — Bill Shankly. 10 — Terry Neill. 11 — Malcolm Allison.

THE PROFESSIONAL
Continued from page 107

SNAPPER SHOWS 'EM!

HE threw himself into the thick of the battle in the midfield as if his life depended on it. Hacked, tripped, banged about, he persevered with a grim determination. Control of the midfield was the key to the whole game.

He spotted Shanks in the clear . . . wondered if the long-legged centre's being there was a fluke or anticipation. He tapped the ball on.

The big lad pounced . . . swerved, beat an opponent and returned the ball quickly to Snapper who was unmarked. Surprised, the centre-half quickly trapped the ball and moved on. He floated a cross into the penalty area. Racing in, Shanks got his head to it but the goalie sprang like a cat and tipped it over the bar.

Snapper regarded the centre with a new respect.

The corner came to nothing but Snapper gained more of the ball and began marshalling attacks. His team-mates took more notice now of his bawling and snapping as he constantly sprayed the ball around probing for weak spots.

Then came his chance. He found himself on the edge of the Skegworth penalty box and onside as Shanks came running through. The centre released the ball to Snapper for the one-two. He hit it back — straight ahead of the big lad.

Hardly altering his stride, Shanks cracked a low drive straight past the 'keeper to bulge the back of the net.

"Good lad . . . nicely placed," grunted Snapper. "Two-one."

"Ta!" Shanks was already racing back upfield for the centre. Time was running out. Only ten minutes remained to snatch the equaliser.

The minutes ticked past. The Ironfield players became more and more desperate. Snapper's cries again fell on deaf ears. Only Shanks seemed to realise what was required.

They were into injury time when Snapper got the ball in midfield. He took it on a few paces, slowed and waited for a defender to come for him . . . he chewed on his gum as if Ironfield were leading by six goals instead of trailing two-one. When the defender was almost on him he slid the ball casually to Shanks. The latter streaked away, weaving right and left before suddenly running for the right-hand corner flag.

Short of the flag he turned, hit the ball high towards the goal to give Snapper time to get in.

As it dropped towards the penalty box Snapper hurled himself forward. Making sure he was above the ball, he struck it hard with his forehead. It hit the ground at the 'keeper's feet. As the man dived for it, it bounced up again, straight over his shoulder for the equaliser.

A second or two later the referee's whistle announced the end of the game.

Snapper grinned at Shanks as they left the field with the excited cheers of their fans ringing in their ears.

"You'll go far, Shanks," he said. "Very, very far. You proved today that you could be another Kenny Dalglish. Today the chips were down . . . and you reacted like a real professional."

"I'm sorry about the other day," Shanks apologised.

" 'S okay."

As Snapper trotted on ahead towards the tunnel, Shanks reflected on the centre-half's words. A professional? Sure . . . but would he ever be the professional that Snapper was? There when needed . . . steadying, plugging the gaps, taking chances when they arose — and mixing it when it was necessary.

As for Snapper, he never took part in the replay which was won 3-2 by Ironfield. He was down with influenza.

The End

Continued from Page 71.

Instructor Ian Aitken helps me with my kit . . .

Hope I don't mix up any of these straps, Ian!

Relax! We won't let you go up until you're put together properly!

Not long to go now!

Mind you, I felt a lot better when my emergency 'chute was strapped on the front!

Someone didn't give me much of a confidence booster by scribbling "L" for learner on my helmet!

Last minute checks . . .

Everything okay?

Yeah — I'm just making sure your static line's properly attached!

Our group of four wait our turn. Frank Davies is our jumpmaster!

Nervous?

You bet!

All aboard!

This is it – no backing down now!

Take off – and I was all set for my very first parachute jump!

We're dropping from 2800 feet! That'll give me over two minutes in the air!

Obviously I wasn't able to take a bulky camera with me, so my final descent was captured on the ground by the Scoop cameraman. What a great feeling it was – once I knew my canopy had opened!

WHEEEE! This is fantastic! Oops! Only about thirty feet to go! Got to get landing drill right!

Phew! That was tremendous! Got to gather in my chute now!

Made it!

OUCH! I'M DOWN!

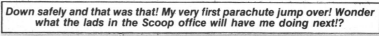

Down safely and that was that! My very first parachute jump over! Wonder what the lads in the Scoop office will have me doing next!?

Here comes Jim – bang on the drop zone!

How did it go?

MAGIC! CAN'T WAIT FOR MY NEXT JUMP!

THE END

Since Barry Sheene first raced competitively in 1969 he has enjoyed the kind of success that even some of his fellow-competitors only dream about. He won his first title—the British 125 c.c. Championship—in 1970 and since then it's been honours all the way.

Here we spotlight just a few of the 'big days' Barry Sheene has enjoyed . . .

BARRY'S BIG DAYS

1975—European 750 c.c. champion.

Segrave Trophy winner in 1977. An award going to the Briton showing the most "skill, courage and initiative" on either land or sea or in the air.

The Segrave Trophy

Barry Sheene

HERON SUZUKI